Puffin Books
The Puffin Book of Brainteasers

Here's a collection of 90 original brainteasers, guaranteed to give you hours of fun and entertainment!

The many different types of puzzles are arranged in order of difficulty from the simple, one-star puzzles, to the quite tricky three-star ones, and if you need help to start off there are hints on how to do each puzzle, and more detailed general suggestions if you get stuck. Each question has a fully explained solution and although none of the puzzles requires special mathematical knowledge you'll soon see that you need a little ingenuity, and must be able to think logically, and to follow the thread of reason wherever it may lead. One thing you can be sure of, there are no hidden catches in the puzzles and there is no place for what is probable or uncertain.

So why not start now and discover the compulsive satisfaction of solving a problem little-by-little and reaching the correct answer? Once you've done one, you'll be sure to want to do more!

Eric Emmet was born in 1909. He won a scholarship to Brasenose College, Oxford, and then taught economics and mathematics at Winchester College. He became Britain's most popular puzzle compiler and contributed to a number of magazines and newspapers. He died in 1980.

Eric Emmet

The Puffin Book of
Brainteasers

Illustrated by Rowan Barnes-Murphy

Puffin Books

PUFFIN BOOKS

Published by the Penguin Group
27 Wrights Lane, London W8 5TZ, England
Viking Penguin Inc., 40 West 23rd Street, New York, New York 10010, USA
Penguin Books Australia Ltd, Ringwood, Victoria, Australia
Penguin Books Canada Ltd, 2801 John Street, Markham, Ontario, Canada L3R 1B4
Penguin Books (NZ) Ltd, 182–190 Wairau Road, Auckland 10, New Zealand

Penguin Books Ltd, Registered Offices: Harmondsworth, Middlesex, England

First published 1976
This abridged edition published 1987
10 9 8 7 6 5 4 3

Printed and bound in Great Britain by
Cox & Wyman Ltd, Reading
Set in Linotype Times by
Rowland Typesetting Ltd, Bury St Edmunds, Suffolk

To all those who helped, by encouraging, by advising, and by checking – especially my wife

Contents

Preface

Most people like solving problems. And not unnaturally most people dislike puzzles or problems which they are unable to do. I hope that this book may help many of you to experience the great pleasure and satisfaction of feeling the mind ticking over and seeing what looks at first sight to be an impossible problem, come to pieces, as it were, in your hands like knotted string or a tricky jigsaw puzzle.

But it is important not to be surprised or disappointed if at first you don't succeed. Not many of these puzzles will be solved by a blinding flash of inspiration. Most of them require a little-by-little method; you start off with something that is of itself very obvious, and indeed the only thing that is not obvious about it may be the fact that it is a possible first step towards the solution; the difficulty, as so often, is not to see that it is so, but to see that it is relevant. And in these puzzles, once you have been successful in doing a few and seeing how they work, or how the mind of the author works, it is easier to see the way to tackle the next one. At the same time you will have the great satisfaction of moving from the very simple to the really quite complicated.

The puzzles in this book are of many different kinds. There are a large number of simple addition and division sums with letters substituted for numbers, and then division sums with most of the letters missing, or with all the letters wrong. We have some cross-number puzzles, and then for those who are not so mathematically minded – although the mathematics required is very simple indeed – there are a lot of football puzzles, some using the old method of scoring, and some using a new method that has been seriously suggested but has not yet, as far as I know, been tried. There are some cricket problems too. And then there are the odd things that happen in our factory and the zany adventures of Professor Knowall and his assistant Serjeant Simple.

These puzzles are arranged in order of difficulty from the very simple, one-star problems, to a few quite tricky three-star ones. In order to avoid the rather daunting feeling of seeing too many of the same kind jostling each other for places in the queue, each section (one-star to three-star) is arranged more or less at random.

For each puzzle there is a fully worked-out solution at the end of the book. And immediately after the puzzles there are a few pages of 'Hints' which will, I hope, help those of you who are unfamiliar with puzzles of this kind to get started. But the hints may not be enough, and for those who need more assistance, there are some general 'Suggestions'. I have said more about this in 'How to Use this Book'.

Many friends have helped with this book, sometimes without knowing they were doing so. I am particularly grateful to David Hall who has checked the puzzles and made many valuable suggestions, to David Wickham, headmaster of Twyford Preparatory School, and to Peter Mills, headmaster of Highfield Preparatory School, who tried some of them out on their pupils and gave me a better idea than I would otherwise have had of just how hard or easy to make them.

With a book of this kind, accurate typing matters a great deal, and I have been very fortunate in having the efficient and willing help of Mrs J. H. Preston.

And most of all I am indebted to my wife for countless suggestions for improvement and, even more important, for her support and encouragement.

How to Use this Book

Those of you who have had no experience of puzzles of this kind before may well find yourselves baffled at first. But don't be discouraged by that. However, you may well ask what you should do.

And the answer is to begin at the beginning from the 'one-star' puzzles, perhaps selecting some that particularly appeal to you, or some in which at a glance you see a starting-point, and move on from there.

This may not happen. It often doesn't. But you have other alternatives open to you.

First of all you might turn to the 'Hints' (which will be found on pages 113–16).

These consist of a few words, or sometimes a couple of lines for each puzzle, suggesting a line of attack, telling you where you might look first.

But these hints may not be enough. You might find, for example, that there are some types of puzzles – perhaps those about football – where you really do not see what is happening and you feel that the only thing to do is to start from square one. In that case I suggest that you look at pages 117–22 where football puzzles are analysed and explained more fully than is possible or desirable in the solutions.

And once you have got the idea, and have learnt to recognize in some of the puzzles some inevitably recurring themes or melodies, you will be armed with the starting-point for many puzzles and may be able to dispense with any assistance. This does not mean that the path to the solutions will then necessarily be an easy one.

You may, at first, be puzzled by the way in which the hints are arranged – first all the puzzles ending in 1, then those ending in 2, and so on. The object of this rather curious exercise is to try to make it less likely that you will be given assistance when you do not want it. If the hints were arranged in the ordinary way and you wanted some assistance, say for Puzzle No. 23, it could very easily happen that you would see by accident the hint for No. 24. But you do not want that. It is possible of course that you may have already decided to do No. 33 just after 23, but as this appears several pages later it would seem unlikely! I hope the method I have used will lessen your chances of being given by accident hints which you do not want.

It may perhaps be worth saying a few words by way of a very general suggestion about the method of tackling these puzzles that is mostly likely to be successful.

It is fairly obvious that a random approach is not likely to produce the right answer often. The best advice I can give you is to have a method, to set out information clearly and perhaps in several different ways, and then, very often, after some trial and error, if the appropriate method has been found it will (or may!) come to pieces in your hands. But success is more likely to come if you remember how important it is to start by reading the question through very carefully indeed.

Don't expect too much too soon. This book would not be worth writing if the puzzles were too easy; and some of the harder three-star ones may really stretch your mind – I hope they do. And as a result you will get a great deal of pleasure when you solve them. Good luck!

Summary

(i) Try some puzzles without any assistance. If you are in doubt as to whether you have got them right look up your answer in the solution.

(ii) If you cannot see how and where to start look up the hint for the puzzle you are doing (pages 113–16) and see if this helps.

(iii) If you are finding the whole thing too hard try looking at the 'Suggestions' (pages 117–34). Choose a kind of puzzle in which you are particularly interested – e.g. football – and try to understand exactly how the solution is arrived at. And don't be surprised if it is necessary to read it more than once.

(iv) The fully worked-out solutions for each puzzle are on pages 135–220.

One-Star Puzzles

1 Uncle Bungle is Stung by a Couple of Bees ★

'Has it ever occurred to you,' said Uncle Bungle to me one day, 'that if I were to be stung by a couple of bees that would add up to my becoming ill.'

Not for the first time I began to think that my uncle was not quite right in the head, but I could see that he was getting rather a lot of pleasure from the fact that I couldn't understand what he was talking about.

'I,' he said, 'and a couple of bees; add them up together and I become ill.'

'Like this,' he said, and he then wrote down for me what I could see was an addition sum.

It looked like this:

$$\begin{array}{r} I \\ B\,B \\ \hline I\,L\,L \end{array}$$

When I understood what he meant I could see that it was an addition sum that even I could manage. Can you? (Each letter stands for a different digit.)

Write down the addition sum with numbers substituted for letters.

2 Football ★

Three Teams, Old Method

Three football teams – A, B and C – are to play each other
once. After some, or perhaps all, of the matches had been
played, a table giving some details of the number of matches played, won, lost, etc., looked like this:

	Played	Won	Lost	Drawn	Goals for	Goals against
A					3	
B		2			2	
C				1		

Find the score in each match.

3 Multiply by Two ★

In the following multiplication by two each letter stands for a different digit. *Find them.*

$$\begin{array}{r} \text{X P M} \\ \underline{2} \\ \text{M A A P} \end{array}$$

4 Addition ★

Letters for Digits, Two Numbers

Below is an addition sum with letters substituted for digits. The same letter stands for the same digit whenever it appears, and different letters stand for different digits.

$$
\begin{array}{r}
F\ C\ F \\
F\ C\ B \\
\hline
B\ B\ J\ C
\end{array}
$$

Write out the sum with numbers substituted for letters.

5 Competition in Our Factory ★

I am the Managing Director of a factory in which, at the time of this story, there were only four employees.

(As the years have passed the number of workers has almost doubled and there are now seven, but this success story is another matter.)

I have always taught those who work for me the importance of competition. Work harder than the next man and run faster than him and you are more likely to be a free man. Especially if the police are after you.

In accordance with these principles my four employees, Alf, Bert, Charlie and Duggie were having a race. It was not easy to discover the result but I did manage to get a certain amount of information.

From a remark that I heard him make it appeared that Bert was not first or third, and Charlie, who does not like Alf much, could not resist boasting that he was two places above him in the race. I also discovered that Duggie was two places below Bert.

In what order did Alf, Bert, Charlie and Duggie come in their race?

6 Football ★

Three Teams, Old Method

After three football teams – A, B and C – had all played
each other once, a bit of paper giving some information
about the matches won, lost, drawn, and the goals for and
against, was found. It read like this:

	Played	Won	Lost	Drawn	Goals for	Goals against
A	2			0	1	1
B	2	2			5	
C	2				2	

Find the score in each match.

7 Division ★

Letters for Digits

In the following division sum each letter stands for a
different digit.

```
          d y
    d r ) r r m
          d r
          d p m
          d p m
```

Rewrite the sum with the letters replaced by digits.

8 Who Pinched My Bike?   ★

I think perhaps I had better introduce myself and the great detective for whom I work.

I am Serjeant Simple, and for many years now I have had the honour of working as the assistant of Professor Knowall. 'What is he a professor of?' you may ask. But perhaps it would really be better to ask what he is *not* a professor of. He has gone to the top in everything he has touched – except perhaps a few unimportant things like tying his shoe-laces and brushing his hair. And how lucky I am to work for him. Although, as a matter of fact, with all modesty, I think you will find that I am not too bad a detective myself.

But let us come to the point. My bicycle had disappeared, and after a lot of discussion, the Professor and I had come to the conclusion that taking into account the opportunities and the motives, and doing a lot of thinking about the characters of the possible suspects, it could only have been done by one of four rather suspicious characters who had recently been seen in and around our house. Their names were Clever, Idle, Loopy and Noddy and it may be taken as certain that one of them was the criminal.

We managed to see each of these four suspects alone, and they made statements as follows:

Clever said that Loopy did it.

Idle said that Loopy had told him that Noddy did it.

Loopy said that Clever did it.

Noddy said 'I know who did it but I am not saying.'

And it was at this point that the Professor's intuition and intelligence were seen at their best. Perhaps it was due to his long experience in similar cases, or to a sixth sense that other lesser mortals do not have. Whatever the explanation he said straight away that Clever and Loopy were not telling the truth but that the other two were. And I am quite sure that he was right. He always is. He also went on to say that Clever and Loopy had quite clearly not told the truth for many years now.

Who pinched my bike?

9 Addition ★

Letters for Digits, Two Numbers

Below is an addition sum with letters substituted for digits.
The same letter stands for the same digit wherever it
appears, and different letters stand for different digits:

$$
\begin{array}{ccc}
P & Y & X \\
P & Y & X \\
\hline
Y & Y & P \\
\end{array}
$$

Write out the sum with numbers substituted for letters.

10 A Cross Number ★

There are no 0's.

Across
1 11 goes into this
3 Each digit is greater than the one before
5 Each digit is 3 greater than the one before

Down
1 Even. Each digit is 2 less than the one before
2 Add the digits together and you get 19
4 Find me!

11 Where was Alf? ★

The distance between my study and the room in which my five employees – Alf, Bert, Charlie, Duggie and Ernie – work is just about ten metres. I found it interesting therefore when I heard that they were organizing a 10-metre race. Ten metres is also curiously enough the distance between their workroom and the great outside world.

I managed to get some information about this race – Duggie, I gathered, was three places above Ernie, and Charlie was not last. Bert's and Charlie's places added up to 8, but there was no mention of Alf.

I discovered after the race the rather curious fact that the person who was last was the one who most frequently assisted me when I called for help.

There were no ties in this race.

Find the order of merit.

12 Addition ★

Letters for Digits, Two Numbers

In the addition sum below letters have been substituted for
digits. The same letter stands for the same digit wherever it
appears, and different letters stand for different digits.

$$
\begin{array}{r}
X\,M\,A \\
X\,X\,A \\
\hline
M\,X\,X
\end{array}
$$

Write out the sum with numbers substituted for letters.

13 Not as it should be ★

If there is one thing that my Uncle Bungle is good at it is
gettings things wrong.

The latest so-called addition sum which he produced for
me to look at was a good example.

It looked like this:

$$
\begin{array}{r}
4\,3 \\
5\,7 \\
\hline
2\,0\,7
\end{array}
$$

My uncle admitted that it was not as it should be. 'But,'
he said, 'all the digits are only 1 out.'

In fact he was right in saying this. Each figure is either 1
more or 1 less than the correct figure.

Find what the addition sum ought to be.

14 Football ★

Three Teams, Old Method

Three football teams, A, B and C, were each to play each other once. After some, or perhaps all, of the matches had been played a table giving some details of matches played, won, lost, etc., looked like this:

	Played	Won	Lost	Drawn	Goals for	Goals against
A						6
B		1		0	4	0
C						3

Find the score in each match.

There are no 0's.

Across
1 A perfect square
3 The same when reversed; digits all even
4 Two of the digits are odd; and each one is at least 2 greater than the one before

Down
1 The sum of the digits is 15
2 The digits are all even; each one is greater than the one before
3 A multiple of 7

16 Cricket ★

Three Teams

A, B and C have been having a cricket competition in which they have all played against each other once.

Points are awarded as follows:
to the side that wins, 10 points;
to the side that wins on the first innings in a drawn match, 6 points;
to the side that loses on the first innings in a drawn match, 2 points;
to each side in a match that is tied, 5 points;
to each side in an uncompleted match that is tied on the first innings, 4 points;
to the side that loses, 0.

A got 7 points; B got 6 points; and C got 15 points.

Find the result of each match.

17 Ernie was Odd ★

Once more Alf, Bert, Charlie, Duggie and Ernie were competing against each other, really, I think, just because they couldn't stop. You are told that Bert was twice as many places above Alf as Duggie was below Charlie. And that Ernie's place was an odd number. There were no ties.

Find the order of merit.

18 Division ★

Some Missing Figures

Uncle Bungle, as anyone who has met him before will know, is a great one for getting things wrong. And when I saw a division sum which he had made up with some of the figures missing, I thought to myself, 'I bet he has done it again.'

But in fact, although it was not so much 'some of the figures missing' as 'nearly all of the figures missing', I discovered later that this time there were no errors. All the figures given, all three of them, were in fact correct.

The sum looked like this:

```
          – 1
  4 –)– – – 9
       – –
       ───
        – –
        – –
       ───
```

Find the complete sum.

19 Cricket ★

Three Teams

A, B and C have all played each other once at cricket.
   Points are awarded as follows:
to the side that wins, 10;
to the side that wins on the first innings in a drawn match, 6;
to the side that loses on the first innings in a drawn match, 2;
to each side for a tie, 5;
to each side for a tie on the first innings in a drawn match, 4;
to the side that loses, 0.
   A, B and C got 12, 10 and 4 points respectively.

Find the result of each match.

20 Division ★

Letters for Digits

In the following division sum each letter stands for a different digit.

```
              z e p
        p d ) y x q x z
              d b
              ─────
              p y x
              z h s
              ─────
                y b z
                y y y
                ─────
                  p y
                  ───
```

Write out the sum with the letters replaced by digits.

21 Stealing, Breaking and Stopping ★

No lives were lost in the crimes with which this story deals, but it is interesting because it is such a good example of the speed with which Professor Knowall's mind works.

The Managing Director of a small factory, who is an old friend of the Professor, had asked him for his assistance.

It seemed that four of his employees, Alf, Bert, Charlie and Duggie were suspected of three rather curious crimes. What had been happening, not once but many times, was that windows had been broken, clocks had been stopped and pencils had been stolen. These misdemeanours were so curious that I thought it would be wise to consult someone who was an expert on the way in which people's minds work. But I had, of course, forgotten that this branch of knowledge was one of the many things which the Professor is a professor of!

'I think you can rely on me, Serjeant Simple,' he said rather crisply, 'to combine detection with psychology in sorting this matter out. I remember that there was a similar case on the Island of Never-Never, and from my experience there and elsewhere I would say that one thing is quite certain, namely, that this is a one-man, one-crime job. Whenever a window has been broken one person, and one person only, has been responsible for it and it is part of the mental illness from which these unfortunate men suffer that if they are in a situation where, for example, there is a clock to be stopped then it will be stopped; and the same thing is true of the other crimes.'

Fortunately the Managing Director of the factory was able to give us a certain amount of precise information.

Apparently in a situation in which Alf, Bert and Charlie were present, a pencil was stolen and a window was broken. And in a situation in which only Alf and Duggie were present, a clock was stopped.

It is obviously difficult for readers who were not present to get the atmosphere of a superbrain ticking over at high speed, which I was able to get, and to enjoy. Let me just say that the Professor solved the problem in less time than it would have taken to break a window.

Assuming that one man specializes in breaking windows, one in stopping clocks and one in stealing pencils, find which of the four men was responsible for each of the three crimes.

22 Only One Out ★

'Well, they are only 1 out,' said Uncle Bungle.

As though that mattered. For he does not seem to realize that if they are wrong they are wrong.

He was referring to a subtraction sum in which, whether by accident or design, all the figures were wrong. They were all 1 more or 1 less than they should have been. Some people say that my Uncle is careless and that he does not see very well, but my own view is that he likes teasing people by getting things wrong.

The figures in Uncle Bungle's subtraction sum were as follows:

$$
\begin{array}{r}
2\ 1\ 6\ 6\ 4\ 8 \\
9\ 0\ 1\ 3\ 5 \\
\hline
1\ 3\ 7\ 8\ 0
\end{array}
$$

Find the correct figures.

23 Addition

Letters for Digits, Three Numbers

Below is an addition sum with letters substituted for digits.
The same letter stands for the same digit wherever it
appears, and different letters stand for different digits.
There are no 1's.

```
    R A X
    A A X
    X A X
    ─────
    M P M
```

Write out the sum with numbers substituted for letters.

24 Football ★

Three Teams, New Method

In the new football league, points are given for goals scored as well as for wins and draws. 10 points are given for a win, 5 points for a draw and 1 point for each goal scored, whatever the result of the match.

Three teams – A, B and C – have each played each other once. And the success of this new method can be seen from the fact that in each game both sides scored at least 1 goal – and more and better goals is the main object of the exercise.

The total number of points for each team was:

A – 9
B – 26
C – 7

Find the score in each match.

25 Football ★

Four Teams, Old Method

A, B, C and D are each to play each other once at football. After some of the matches had been played a table giving some of the figures of matches played, won, lost, drawn, etc., looked like this:

	Played	Won	Lost	Drawn	Goals for	Goals against	Points
A	1					1	
B	1				3		2
C					2	2	
D	3				4		3

(2 points are given for a win, and 1 point for a draw.)

Find the score in each match.

26 Who Does What in Our Factory ★

This story is about the early days of our factory, just after we had made the great expansion to seven employees.

Alf, Bert, Charlie, Duggie, Ernie, Fred and George are their names; and their jobs, not necessarily respectively, are the Door-Opener, the Door-Shutter, the Door-Knob-Polisher, the Bottle-Washer, the Welfare Officer, the Sweeper-Upper and last but, in spite of what some people say, not least, the Worker.

Alf was not the Bottle-Washer or the Worker; and Fred was not the Door-Knob-Polisher, the Door-Opener or the Worker.

Bert was either the Welfare Officer, the Door-Shutter or the Sweeper-Upper; and Duggie was either the Door-Knob-Polisher or the Sweeper-Upper.

The Door-Shutter was not Bert, Charlie or George; and the Sweeper-Upper was not Bert, Ernie or Fred. But the Door-Opener was either Alf, Charlie or Fred.

The Door-Knob-Polisher was not Charlie, Duggie or George; and the Worker was not Charlie or George.

Find each of my employees' occupations.

27 Uncle Bungle Shows that ★ He Can Get Division Sums Wrong Too!

Uncle Bungle always wants to do better than other people or sometimes just better than himself. We have seen a subtraction sum of his with all the figures wrong and he has now produced a long division sum with all the figures wrong too. Does he do it on purpose, I wonder, or can he just not help it?

Perhaps we shall never know the answer to this question but it is at least rather odd that in this sum, like the addition sum, all the digits are just 1 out, that is to say they are 1 more or 1 less than they should be.

The sum looks like this:

```
            2 9
      8 4 )2 2 2 3
            6 2
          ───────
          6 9 3
          4 9 3
          ───────
```

Find the correct figures.

28 Addition ★

Letters for Digits, Two Numbers

Below is an addition sum with letters substituted for digits. The same letter stands for the same digit wherever it appears, and different letters stand for different digits.

$$
\begin{array}{r}
R\,P\,A\,P \\
A\,B\,B\,M \\
\hline
R\,R\,R\,P \\
\end{array}
$$

Write out the sum with numbers substituted for letters.

29 Football ★

Three Teams, New Method

In order to encourage more goals in football a new method
has been devised in which not only the result counts but also
the number of goals scored.

In this method 10 points are awarded for a win, 5 points
for a draw, and 1 point for each goal scored whatever the
result of the match.

In a recent competition between three teams – A, B and
C – in which they all played each other once, the points
which each team got were as follows:

A – 22
B – 15
C – 8

In each match each side scored at least 1 goal, but not
more than 7 were scored by both teams. B did not lose a
match.

Find the score in each game.

30 The Good Worker ★

At the time with which this story deals three of the employees in our factory – Ernie, Fred and George – had the jobs, not necessarily respectively, of Door-Opener, Door-Shutter and Worker.

Perhaps because of the in-and-out nature of their jobs the Door-Opener and the Door-Shutter had got, I'm afraid, into the habit of telling lies. But not the Worker. He did a good job and he told the truth.

They spoke as follows:

Ernie: 'George is the Door-Shutter.'
Fred: 'Ernie is the Door-Opener.'
George: 'Fred is the Worker.'

Find the jobs of my three employees.

31 Still Only One Out ★

In his latest rather curious-looking subtraction sum Uncle
Bungle makes no secret of what he is trying to do. The
object of the exercise as far as he is concerned is to deceive
and to conceal.

But all the figures are only 1 out, and I am sure that my
readers will be intelligent enough to call Uncle Bungle's
bluff, as it were, and to produce the correct figures.

The incorrect figures were:

$$
\begin{array}{r}
2\ 9\ 1\ 0 \\
1\ 4\ 9\ 7 \\
\hline
2\ 1\ 0\ 6
\end{array}
$$

Find the correct figures.

32 Football ★

Four Teams, New Method

The new method of rewarding goals in football matches, irrespective of who wins, is becoming more and more popular.

Under this method 10 points are awarded for a win, 5 points for a draw, and 1 point for each goal that the team scores, irrespective of the result of the match. It is interesting to notice the extent to which more goals continue to be scored; in the latest competition, each side scored at least one goal in every match.

The four teams, A, B, C and D are eventually all going to play each other once. The situation when all but two matches had been played was as follows:

A – 20 points
B – 4 points
C – 1 point
D – 30 points.

Find the score in each match.

33 Who was X?

When one of my employees told me the other day that he had come fourth in a fifty metre race I must say that I was rather surprised. X, as I shall call him for the moment, had always been the slowest in every way of the seven members of our factory, and I could not imagine him coming anywhere but last in any competition.

But it was not long before I discovered that last in fact was where he had come, for there were only four people in the race – namely Alf, Charlie, Ernie and George.

But the reader might like to have enough information to find out exactly what did happen.

Charlie was as many places behind Ernie as George was before Alf.

Ernie was not first and Alf was not second.

Who was X? And in what order did they all come in the race?

50

34 Cricket ★

Three Teams

A, B and C have all played each other once at cricket.
Points are awarded as follows:
to the side that wins, 10;
to the side that wins on the first innings in a drawn match, 6;
to the side that loses on the first innings in a drawn match, 2;
to each side for a tie, 5;
to the side that loses, 0.
A, B and C got 11, 10 and 7 points respectively.

Find the result of each match.

35 Division ★

Some Missing Figures

A division sum.

```
        - 5 -
 - - )6 - - -
      - -
      - - -
        - -
       ----
        - 7 -
        - - -
```

Find the missing digits.

36 Addition ★

Letters for Digits, Two Numbers

Below is an addition sum with letters substituted for digits. The same letter stands for the same digit wherever it appears, and different letters stand for different digits.

```
  Z B B
  B Y B
  -----
  C Z Z
```

Write out the sum with numbers substituted for letters.

37 The Running-Backward Race ★

The workers in my factory realize very well that in order to fit themselves for a modern industrial world they must compete. It seems sensible to them that they should get practice in this by competing against each other.

The latest competition I have organized has been a running-backward race, in which Alf, Bert, Charlie, Duggie and Ernie have been trying to see who can move fastest in the wrong direction.

Duggie beat Bert by as many places as Alf beat Charlie, and Bert beat Charlie.

Ernie was not first or third, and Bert was not second.

Find the order in which they came in the race.

Two-Star Puzzles

38 Football

Four Teams, Old Method

Four football teams – A, B, C and D – are all to play each other once.

After some – or perhaps all – of the matches have been played a table giving some details of the matches played, won, lost, etc., looked like this:

	Played	Won	Lost	Drawn	Goals for	Goals against
A		0		1	3	3
B						
C	3				7	5
D			0	0	2	1

Find the score in each match.

39 Addition

Letters for Digits, Two Numbers

Below is an addition sum with letters substituted for digits. The same letter stands for the same digit wherever it appears, and different letters stand for different digits.

$$\begin{array}{r} R\,A\,A\,P \\ G\,G\,A\,P \\ \hline P\,M\,B\,M\,R \end{array}$$

Write out the sum with numbers substituted for letters.

40 All is Confusion – but the ★★ Bottle-Washer was Third

I fear that as Managing Director of our factory I seem to have lost my touch. Events have happened so quickly and my workers – Alf, Bert, Charlie, Duggie and Ernie – seem to have changed their jobs so frequently that I really hardly know who is what. I do know, however, that their jobs at the moment are – in no particular order – those of Bottle-Washer, Door-Opener, Door-Shutter, Door-Knob-Polisher and last, and unfortunately rather often least, Worker.

They have been having a competition amongst each other for something or other (and it may give you some idea of the state I am in that I really don't know what) and I have been able to get hold of a certain amount of information about this. I do know that in accordance with the long-standing custom of the company there were no ties.

The information that I was able to get hold of was as follows:

1 Bert was three places above the Door-Opener, who was below Alf.
2 None of the three doormen was fifth.
3 The Door-Knob-Polisher was three places above Charlie.
4 Duggie was one place below the Door-Shutter.
5 Ernie's place was even.
6 The Bottle-Washer was third.

I hope that from this information you will be able to discover in what order Alf, Bert, Charlie, Duggie and Ernie came in this competition and what their jobs were.

41 Multiply by 4 ★★

In the following multiplication each letter stands for a different digit. *Find them*.

$$
\begin{array}{r}
C\ B\ D\ F \\
4 \\
\hline
D\ F\ D\ E\ D
\end{array}
$$

42 Cause and Effect ★ ★

It is perhaps rather difficult to know what Professor Knowall is best at. But one thing at which he is certainly very good indeed (and indeed as a detective he should be) is the tracing of cause and effect.

'Remember, my dear Serjeant Simple,' as he has so often said to me, 'that generally speaking the same cause has usually the same effect or effects. If I stand in the rain without any clothes I shall get wet. But I may also get wet in a lot of other ways, for example by diving into the sea. In other words, the same event may be preceded by many different causes.'

It was a great piece of luck that next day I had a chance to show my new cause-and-effect skill in a rather tricky piece of detection. I won't burden the reader with the details, but will put the facts down just as the Professor suggested I should with the causes followed by the possible effects.

To cut all sorts of long stories short there were six possible causes (A, B, C, D, E, F) and they were followed by four possible effects; fortunately there was every reason to believe that each effect had just one single cause.

The details were as follows:

A, C, F were followed by q and r.
B, C, D, F were followed by s and r.
B, D, E were followed by p and s.
A, D, E, F were followed by p and q.

What were the causes of p, q, r, s?

43 Two, Four, Six, Eight ★★

Uncle Bungle sings a song:
'One of these is surely wrong.
Choose, as you'll appreciate:
Two or Four or Six or Eight?'

```
              2 –
    4 – )– – – 8
        – – –
        ———
          – –
          6 –
```

Which of these figures was 'surely wrong'?

Find the correct division sum.

44 Football

Three Teams, Old Method

Three football teams – A, B and C – are to play each other once. After some – or perhaps all – of the matches have been played a piece of paper giving some details of matches played, won, lost, etc., looked like this:

	Played	Won	Lost	Drawn	Goals for	Goals against
A					5	4
B				1	2	
C					6	4

Find the score in each match.

45 A Cross Number

There are no 0's.

Across
1 A factor of 3 Across
3 A perfect square
5 The sum of the digits is 12. They are all even and all different

Down
1 A multiple of 4 Down
2 Each digit is greater than the one before
4 A perfect square

46 A Competition ★ ★

Alf, Bert, Charlie, Duggie and Ernie have been having a competition with each other, in which there are no ties.

You are told that Alf was as many places above Bert as Duggie was above Ernie; and that neither Charlie nor Ernie was third or fifth.

Find their order.

47 Division ★★

Figures All Wrong

In the following, obviously incorrect, division sum the pattern is correct, but all the figures are 1 out, that is they are 1 more or 1 less than the correct figures. The sum comes out exactly.

```
        3 8
2 3 ) 8 7 5
      7 7
      ─────
      2 1 5
      4 1 5
      ─────
```

Find the correct figures.

48 Football ★ ★

Three Teams, New Method

What attracts people to watch football is goals being scored. And the authorities have been thinking for a long time of methods whereby the scoring of more goals might be encouraged.

One suggestion that has been made involves a change in the way that points are awarded. The idea is that 10 points should be awarded for a win, 5 points for a draw, and 1 point for each goal scored, whatever the result of the match. Therefore even if you are losing 0–5 and have no hope of winning, a goal scored might make all the difference between promotion and non-promotion.

This method was tried out on a small scale and its success can be judged from the fact that each side scored at least one goal in every match. There were only three sides playing and eventually they are all going to play each other once. A had scored 8 points, B had scored 14 points, and C had scored 9 points.

Find the score in each match.

49 Serjeant Simple Loses his Wallet

I could not think where I had left it. My wallet, I mean. It contained several things of sentimental value and also a little bit of money in which I am quite interested.

Professor Knowall was not being very helpful.

'If you can't find your own wallet, how are you going to find criminals, my dear Serjeant Simple?' he said.

And although I was pretty certain that he knew where it was, all I could persuade him to do was to give me a few clues.

They went like this:

(1) If you don't fail to find your wallet it's because you haven't looked in the deep freeze.

(2) If you can't find your wallet it's because you haven't looked behind the desk.

(3) You can't both find your wallet and not fail to look in the cycle shed.

I am afraid this was too much for me, but perhaps the reader may be able to make suggestions as to where I should look for my wallet.

50 A Cross Number

There are no 0's.

Across
1 A factor of 3 Across
3 An odd number. Each digit is greater than the one before
5 1 Down multiplied by an even number

Down
1 See 5 Across
2 We seem to have this somewhere else
4 A perfect square

51 The Factory Dinner-Party ★★

This story is about the occasion, many years ago now, when the five original workers in my factory were, for the first time, to be paid for the work which they did. Before this they had had hopes and promises, free suppers, and a permanent invitation to sleep in the stables, but no cash. After all it seemed reasonable to wait until we had actually sold some of our products. But now this great event had actually happened, and if anything ever called for a celebration, this was surely it.

So my five employees – Alf, Bert, Charlie, Duggie and Ernie, whose jobs at that time, but in no particular order, were the Bottle-Washer, the Door-Opener, the Door-Shutter, the Welfare Officer and the Worker – were sitting round a circular table waiting for their employer, that is myself, to give them dinner.

You might be interested to know just how they were sitting and what their jobs were.

No two men, the initial letters of whose names were next to each other in the alphabet, were sitting next to each other at the table, and Charlie does not have Alf sitting on his right. Bert is sitting between the Welfare Officer and the Door-Shutter, and the two doormen (the Door-Shutter and the Door-Opener), one of whom is Duggie, are not sitting next to each other. You are also told that Alf is not the Bottle-Washer.

Show in a diagram where my employees were sitting and what their jobs were.

52 Division

Letters for Digits

In the following division sum each letter stands for a different digit.

```
            d k g b
      ┌─────────────
d h ) g d n s f s
        g g n
        ─────
        s f s
        g h k
        ─────
          n f
          d h
          ───
          d g s
          d g s
```

Find the sum with the letters replaced by digits.

There are no 0's.

Across
1 Each digit is greater than the one before
4 The same when reversed. Odd
5 A perfect square

Down
1 A perfect square
2 Sum of digits is 16
3 Each digit is greater than the one before

A Multiplication

In the following multiplication sum letters have been substituted for digits, and of course the same letters stand for
the same digits whenever they occur, and different letters
stand for different digits.

```
P M M T P
        P
---------
N P T R P T
```

You are told that P = 2T.

Find the digits for which the letters stand.

55 Uncle Bungle's Football Puzzle ★★

My Uncle Bungle is very keen on games, especially on football, and now that he is a pretty elderly gentleman he has taken to making up puzzles about his favourite game.

In his latest one about four teams, A, B, C and D, who are eventually going to play each other once, I'm afraid that a large number of the figures have just been left out. I never quite know whether this is due to my uncle's carelessness (and he is indeed a very careless man), or whether he is being rather clever in giving just the amount of information that is needed.

Whatever it is you might like to find out the score in the matches that have been played between four teams A, B, C and D.

The information that my uncle gave was as follows:

	Played	Won	Lost	Drawn	Goals for	Goals against
A		2			2	
B			0	0	4	3
C					5	3
D	3					

Find the score in each match.

56 Addition ★★

Letters for Digits, Two Numbers

Below is an addition sum with letters substituted for digits. The same letter stands for the same digit wherever it appears, and different letters stand for different digits.

```
R X E K P P
R X X R P P
───────────
H R B H P H
```

Write out the sum with numbers substituted for letters.

57 Cricket

Three Teams

A, B and C have all played each other once at cricket.
Points are awarded as follows:
to the side that wins, 10;
to the side that wins on the first innings in a drawn match, 6;
to the side that loses on the first innings in a drawn match, 2;
to each side for a tie, 5;
to each side for a tie on the first innings in a drawn match, 4;
to the side that loses, 0.

I was told that A got 3 points, that B got 11, and that C got 13. But I learnt subsequently that two of these figures were wrong, though neither of them was more than 2 out. I was also able to discover that no match was won.

Find the result of each match.

58 Division ★★

Figures All Wrong

In the following, obviously incorrect, division sum, the
pattern is correct, but all the figures are 1 out, that is they
are 1 more or 1 less than the correct figures. The sum comes
out exactly.

```
            3 4
      1 4 ) 6 1 8
            5 5
            ———
            7 8
            5 8
            ———
```

Find the correct figures.

59 Football ★★

Four Teams, Old Method

Four football teams – A, B, C and D – are all to play each
other once. After some of the matches have been played a
table giving some details of the number of matches played,
won, lost, etc., looked like this:

	Played	Won	Lost	Drawn	Goals for	Goals against
A				2		
B			1		4	
C				0	1	1
D	1					3

Find the score in each match.

60 Multiply by 3 ★★

In the following multiplication each letter stands for a different digit. *Find them.*

$$
\begin{array}{r}
L\,D\,C\,F\,L \\
3 \\
\hline
H\,J\,D\,H\,H\,L
\end{array}
$$

61 Uncle Bungle Moves to Addition ★★

Uncle Bungle has now, I think, made the point that he can get a subtraction wrong, but he always likes to move to fresh fields and different sums, and he has just been showing that what he can do for subtraction he can also do for addition.

He has made up an addition sum in which all the figures are 1 wrong, that is 1 more or 1 less than the correct figure.

It looks like this:

$$
\begin{array}{r}
6\,3\,2\,3 \\
9\,6\,0\,6 \\
\hline
2\,3\,2\,5\,6
\end{array}
$$

Find the correct addition sum.

There are no 0's.

Across
1 The square of an odd number
3 Half 1 Down
4 The same when reversed

Down
1 Twice 3 Across
2 Digits all go up or all go down
The difference between the first and second digits is the
same as the difference between the second and third.

63 Addition ★ ★

Letters for Digits, Two Numbers

In the addition sum below the digits have been replaced by letters. The same letter stands for the same digit wherever it appears, and different letters stand for different digits.

```
Y A B A E W T P
Y A W H P T T H
───────────────
J P K P J E Y A H
```

Write out the sum with numbers substituted for letters.

64 Division ★ ★

Some Missing Figures

A division sum.

```
        – 7 –
– – )– – – – 1
     – – 4
     ───────
     – – –
       – –
       ───
       – –
       ───
       – –
       ───
```

Find the missing digits.

65 Right or Wrong? ★★

I was rather pleased with the latest puzzle which I had made up about the five workers in our factory having a competition, and I hastened to show it to a friend of mine.

It went like this:

'Alf, Bert, Charlie, Duggie and Ernie made statements about their order in a competition they were having. They spoke as follows:

A: "Charlie was higher than I was."
B: "I was second or third."
C: "Duggie was higher than Ernie."
D: "I was fourth or fifth."
E: "Alf was higher than Bert."'

I was surprised however to see how quickly my friend claimed to have done it.

When I looked at my notes however his answer did not agree with mine – and then, suddenly, I saw the light. 'Oh, by the way,' I said, 'I forgot to tell you that all those statements are wrong.'

What was the order my friend got, assuming that all the statements were true? And what was the order he would have got assuming that they were all false?

66 Football

Four Teams, Old Method

Four football teams – A, B, C and D – are all to play each
other once. After some of the matches have been played a
table giving some details of the matches played, won, lost,
etc., looked like this:

	Played	Won	Lost	Drawn	Goals for	Goals against
A	2					
B				2	5	5
C	2		1		3	1
D				1		2

Find the score in each match.

67 Cricket

Three Teams

A, B and C have all played each other once at cricket.
   Points are awarded as follows:
to the side that wins, 10;
to the side that wins on the first innings in a drawn match, 6;
to the side that loses on the first innings in a drawn match, 2;
to each side for a tie, 5;
to each side for a tie on the first innings in a drawn match, 4;
to the side that loses, 0.
   A, B and C got 12, 6 and 10 points respectively.

Find the result of each match.

68 Letters for Digits ★★

A Multiplication

In the multiplication sum below letters have been substituted for digits. The same letter stands for the same digit wherever it appears, and different letters stand for different digits.

$$
\begin{array}{r}
\text{W V G E} \\
\times \qquad \text{W} \\
\hline
\text{T F E W}
\end{array}
$$

You are told that W is an odd number and that there are no 0's.

Find the digits for which the letters stand.

69 A Cross Number

There are no 0's.

Across
1 The sum of the digits is 11
3 Each digit is 2 greater than the one before
5 A perfect square

Down
1 The same when reversed
2 An even number. Each digit is less than the one before
4 An even number, and a multiple of 11

70 Addition ★ ★

Letters for Digits, Three Numbers

In the following sum letters have been substituted for
digits, and three five-figure numbers have been added
together. The same letter stands for the same digit wherever it appears, and different letters stand for different
digits.

$$
\begin{array}{r}
Y\,R\,R\,M\,P \\
Y\,R\,P\,M\,P \\
Y\,R\,Y\,M\,P \\
\hline
R\,Y\,M\,A\,B\,P
\end{array}
$$

Write out the sum with numbers substituted for letters.

71 Uncle Bungle Passes through a Bad Patch ★★

Sometimes he gets things right and sometimes he doesn't, but just at the moment I am afraid that Uncle Bungle seems to be passing through a bad patch. In the latest division sum which he has produced only four figures were given and to get one of them wrong seems to me an unusually high percentage. Not, mind you, that he can't do better than that, for there have been occasions when he has got all the figures wrong!

The division sum that he produced looked like this:

```
          - 2
  5 - ) 5 - - -
         - - -
         ─────
           - -
           - 9
```

Which figure was wrong? What should the correct division sum have been?

Three-Star Puzzles

72 Multiply by 5

In the following multiplication by 5 each letter stands for a different digit. *Find them.*

$$\begin{array}{r} X\ Q\ R\ X\ F\ X\ A \\ 5 \\ \hline A\ M\ Q\ K\ D\ F\ Q \end{array}$$

73 Uncle Bungle Gets
'One in Three' Wrong

I have often thought that Uncle Bungle has much in common with the Ancient Mariner. He may not have a long grey beard, but he has certainly got a 'glittering eye'.

In his famous poem Coleridge describes how this character stopped 'one in three'. My uncle is certainly likely to do this when he gets the chance, with the same motives and in the same way as his better known predecessor. And I think that the Ancient Mariner would be quite likely to get his sums wrong.

But be that as it may, in his latest long division sum my Uncle has managed to get one of the three figures given wrong. And what is left looks like this:

Which figure is wrong? Find the correct division sum.

There are no 0's.

Across
1 A perfect square
4 The same when reversed
5 Even. Sum of digits is 11

Down
1 A perfect square
2 Sum of digits is 16
3 Each digit is 2 greater than the digit before

75 Addition

Letters for Digits, Two Numbers

Below is an addition sum with letters substituted for digits. The same letter stands for the same digit wherever it appears, and different letters stand for different digits.

X J D F C
C D F C C

J J J Y J

Write out the sum with numbers substituted for letters.

76 Bert was not First ★ ★ ★

Alf, Bert, Charlie, Duggie, Ernie and Fred have been having a competition again, but this time it was a very nice simple one. They were running 100 metres for a small prize given by the Managing Director, and I am glad to say that there were no ties as this might have complicated the issue.

You might be interested to hear something about the results.

Charlie was as many places behind Fred as Bert was before Alf, but the difference between Charlie and Fred was more than one.

Bert was not first, and Fred was not fourth, and neither Alf nor Charlie was last. The number of Duggie's place was half the number of Ernie's.

In what order did the six of them come in the 100-metre race?

77 Football

Five Teams, Old Method

Five football teams, A, B, C, D and E, are to play each other once. After some of the matches have been played a table giving some details of matches played, won, lost, etc., looked like this:

	Played	Won	Lost	Drawn	Goals for	Goals against
A			1	0	1	2
B			1			5
C	2		1		7	4
D		1		0	2	2
E		2		0	5	2

Find the score in each match.

78 Division ★ ★ ★

Letters for Digits

In the following division sum each letter stands for a different digit.

```
           k n m d
   h e ) e n d j n
         c g
         ─────
         k d
         d k
         ─────
           p j
           g m
           ─────
             m n
             m h
             ───
               h
```

Find the sum with the letters replaced by digits.

79 Cricket

Four Teams

Four teams – A, B, C and D – have each played each other
once at cricket.

    Points are given as follows:
to the side that wins, 10;
to the side that wins on the first innings in a drawn match, 6;
to the side that loses on the first innings in a drawn match, 2;
to each side for a tie, 5;
to the side that loses, 0.

    A, B, C and D got 25, 2, 8 and 21 points respectively.

Find the result of each match.

80 Addition

Letters for Digits, Three Numbers

In the addition sum below the digits have been replaced by
letters. The same letter stands for the same digit wherever it
appears, and different letters stand for different digits.

```
G G J  D G F F
G G G P B F F
G G B D G F F
```

```
Z N Y H P B G
```

Write out the sum with numbers substituted for letters.

There are no 0's.

Across

1 A factor of 5 Across
3 Even
5 The square of 4 Down

Down

1 Sum of digits is 15
2 Each digit is 2 greater than the digit before
4 The second digit is greater than the first

82 Football

Four Teams, New Method

Goals are what the public goes to see, and goals are what they have been enjoying as a result of the new football method.

In this method 10 points are awarded for a win, 5 points for a draw, and 1 point for each goal scored whatever the result of the game.

A, B, C and D are eventually going to play each other once. After all but two of the matches had been played, the situation was as follows:

A – 7 points
B – 8 points
C – 39 points
D – 3 points

Each side scored at least 1 goal in every match, but not more than 7 goals were scored in any game.

Find the scores in all the matches.

83 Our Factory – Logic and Charm

It has always been my principle that if the workers in my factory are going to compete (and compete they certainly do), then they should try to show their superiority in things that really matter.

When Alf told me that he and Bert, Charlie, Duggie and Ernie were going to have a test to produce an order of merit in logic and in charm, I made it clear that this idea met with the complete approval of the Managing Director.

After all, some people think that logic matters, and a great deal of charm may often be needed by my not very intelligent employees to persuade people that their particular brand of logic makes sense.

I was given some information about the order of merit in these two subjects, in which there were no ties.

As follows:

(1) Bert is as many places above Duggie in logic as Duggie is above Bert in charm. But neither Bert nor Duggie is first in either of them.

(2) Ernie is below Bert in charm and Bert is above Ernie in logic.

(3) Alf is less logical than Charlie, and Charlie is less charming than Alf.

(4) Ernie is neither the least logical nor the least charming.

Find their order of merit in logic and in charm.

84 Bungle Blunders ★★★

Bungle blunders once again.
'Which is wrong?' he cries in vain.
'Eight or six or five or two?'
That's a puzzle just for you.

```
          8 –
  – 2 ) – – 6
        – 5
       ——————
        – –
       ——————
        – –
```

One of the figures is wrong. Which one?

Find the correct division sum.

85 Cricket

Five Teams

A, B, C, D and E are all to play each other once at cricket.
  Points are awarded as follows:
to the side that wins, 10;
to the side that wins on the first innings in a drawn match, 6;
to the side that loses on the first innings in a drawn match, 2;
to each side for a tie, 5;
to each side for a tie on the first innings in a drawn match, 4;
to the side that loses, 0.

  A, B, C, D and E got 6, 35, 11, 12 and 2 points respectively.

  You are told that A and C only played two matches, and that D won one of theirs. C did not play E.

  Find the result of each match.

Letters for Digits, Three Numbers

In the addition sum below the digits have been replaced by
letters. The same letter stands for the same digit wherever it
appears, and different letters stand for different digits.

```
B Y T Z B X D D
B S V Z D B D D
B B S Z D B D D
───────────────
X V N P P N B B
```

Write out the sum with numbers substituted for letters.

87 What Done It? ★★★

Professor Knowall is prepared to investigate all sorts of mistakes or misdemeanours, not only 'Who Done It?' but also 'What Done It?', so I therefore asked him if he could help me investigate the trouble in my car.

There seemed to be three separate things that were going wrong, or rather made the car less satisfactory than the makers intended it should be.

It was all right when it was not running, but when the engine was on and I tried to get things to work, there was a high-pitched scream, a rumble and a dull thud.

I felt pretty certain that the causes of these things were one of the following: the windscreen wipers, opening the left-hand window, putting on the handbrake, pulling the button that said 'Push Heater' or opening the right-hand window.

But I did not see how to find out which caused which.

But, as I knew he would, the Professor was able to solve my little problem.

'What you want, my dear Serjeant Simple,' he said, 'is a controlled experiment.'

I must admit that I did not quite understand what he meant by this, but I knew that I could rely upon him to explain it and to do whatever was necessary. To cut a long story short the result of our controlled experiment was as follows:

When we opened the left-hand window, put on the handbrake, and also opened the right-hand window, the result was the high-pitched scream and the rumble.

The result of turning on the windscreen wipers, putting on the handbrake, pulling the 'Push Heater' button, and opening the right-hand window, was a rumble and a dull thud.

We then tried the windscreen wipers, together with the opening of the left-hand window, putting on the handbrake, and pulling the 'Push Heater' button. The result was the high-pitched scream and the dull thud.

Our last experiment was the windscreen wipers again, the opening of both the left-hand and the right-hand windows, and putting on the handbrake. We then had what one might describe as the complete orchestra, that is to say the high-pitched scream, the rumble and the dull thud.

It will not surprise my readers to hear that I did not quite know what to do with this evidence, but perhaps they will.

On the assumption that the three noises which we are investigating each have one single cause, find out what is responsible for the high-pitched scream, the rumble and the dull thud.

88 Uncle Bungle Multiplies ★★★

From getting addition and subtraction sums wrong it is only a short step to getting multiplication sums wrong. And Uncle Bungle has now taken this step.

I am glad to say however that he has had the sense not to overdo things and all the figures are only 1 out.

It looked like this:

```
  1 6 6 3
        3
─────────
2 1 3 7 9
```

Find the correct sum.

89 Football

Four Teams, New Method

The new method of rewarding goals scored in football goes from strength to strength, and the score looks very different from the 0–0 and 1–0 of the old days.

Under this method 10 points are awarded for a win, 5 points for a draw, and 1 point for each goal scored. In the latest competition each side scored at least 1 goal in every match and in a match that was drawn each side scored at least 2 goals.

Points were awarded as follows:

A – 7
B – 13
C – 20
D – 4

Not more than 6 goals were scored in any match.

Find the score in each match.

90 Addition

Letters for Digits, Three Numbers

Below is an addition sum with letters substituted for digits. The same letter stands for the same digit wherever it appears, and different letters stand for different digits.

```
  L P B R R
  T L S R R
  S B R R R
  ---------
  R L M P L
```

Write out the sum with numbers substituted for letters.

Hints

For puzzles ending in 1 (i.e., 1, 11, 21, 31 . . . 81)

1 Think what 'I' must be.
11 Start by considering Bert's and Charlie's places.
21 Think who was there when there was *no* pencil stealing, etc.
31 Consider the last column, and move to the left.
41 What is D?
51 Think what follows from the fact that 'C does have not A on his right'.
61 Consider figures on the right and then move to the left.
71 Look for two figures that cannot both be right. And then look for two more figures that cannot both be right.
81 Look at 5 Across, 4 Down and 3 Across.

For puzzles ending in 2 (i.e., 2, 12, 22, 32 . . . 82)

2 Look at B's games.
12 What can you say about M?
22 Start by considering the last line down and then move to the left.
32 Start by finding what points each side got for wins or draws.
42 Consider what p, for example, is *not* caused by.
52 Find 0 and 1.
62 Consider 3 Across and 1 Down.
72 Start by finding X.
82 Start with C.

For puzzles ending in 3 (i.e., 3, 13, 23, 33 . . . 83)

3   What can you say about M, and then P?

13   Start by considering the first two digits in the answer.

23   Remembering that there are no 1's; look at the first line down.

33   What can you say about places where they are *not*?

43   Look for mistakes. Two figures will be involved. How do you find which is wrong?

53   Look at 1 Down and 4 Across.

63   Go for J and P.

73   Find two figures that cannot both be right. How can you find which is wrong?

83   Set out the possibilities for logic and charm. What can you say about who was first?

For puzzles ending in 4 (i.e., 4, 14, 24, 34 . . . 84)

4   What is B? What is F?

14   Consider B.

24   How many points did each side get for wins and draws?

34   Consider how A can have got their points.

44   Compare A's and B's goals for, with C's goals against. What can you say about scores in A v. B?

54   Look at the last line down.

64   The 7 in the answer should tell you quite a lot about the divisor.

74   Look at 5 Across and 3 Down.

84   Find two figures that cannot both be right. And then two more figures that cannot both be right.

For puzzles ending in 5 (i.e., 5, 15, 25, 35 . . . 85)

5   Draw a diagram showing their possible places.

15   Consider 2 Down and 1 Across.

25   Who did C play?

35   The divisor times 5 contains two figures. What can you say about the divisor?

45 Consider 3 Across and 4 Down.
55 How many matches did B play?
65 Put the facts down clearly.
75 Look at the last and first columns.
85 Consider B's games and results.

For puzzles ending in 6 (i.e., 6, 16, 26, 36 . . . 86)

6   What were the scores in A's two games?
16 How can A have got their points?
26 Draw a diagram with names down and jobs across.
36 Think what you can say about B.
46 Draw up a table setting out the possibilities.
56 Go for P.
66 Consider C.
76 Set out possibilities neatly.
86 What can you say about B?

For puzzles ending in 7 (i.e., 7, 17, 27, 37 . . . 87)

7   What can you say about the first figure in the answer?
17 'Bert was twice as many places above Alf, as Duggie was below Charlie.' Set out the possibilities of this.
27 Think what you can say about the divisor.
37 Suppose E was second.
47 How must the divisor start?
57 There is no way of getting certain points. Which?
67 Consider the different ways in which A can have got their points.
77 What can you say about B's matches?
87 Remember that each noise has a *single* cause.

For puzzles ending in 8 (i.e., 8, 18, 28, 38 . . . 88)

8   Think what follows from the fact that Clever and Loopy are liars.
18 From the fact that the second figure in answer is 1, what can you say about the divisor?

115

28 What is R?

38 Consider D.

48 What is the number of points got from wins and draws?

58 How must the divisor start?

68 Suppose that W is 5.

78 Try to find how the divisor starts.

88 Think what 9 must be.

For puzzles ending in 9 (i.e., 9, 19, 29, 39 . . . 89)

9 What can you say about Y?

19 Consider the possibilities for A's points.

29 How many points did B and C get for wins and draws and for goals?

39 Get P and then R.

49 Remember that from 'If p, then q' it does *not* follow that 'If q, then p'.

59 What can you say about C?

69 Consider 5 Across. Remember that 4 Down and 2 Down are both even.

79 Find the number of points for wins and draws.

89 Think how the points must be divided between wins and draws on the one hand and goals on the other.

For puzzles ending in 0 (i.e., 10, 20, 30, 40 . . . 90)

10 What can you say about the last digit in 1 Down?

20 What is y?

30 Consider George's statement.

40 Set the information out neatly, and start from the fact that the Bottle-Washer was third.

50 Look at 4 Down and 3 Across.

60 Look on the right, and find L.

70 Go for P and R.

80 Go for G.

90 Go for R.

Suggestions

Football, Old Method

The method of setting out a football table is best explained
by looking at a simple situation in which A and B play each
other once only.

Thus: (i)

	Played	Won	Lost	Drawn	Goals for	Goals against
A	1	1	0	0	4	2
B	1	0	1	0	2	4

It is easy to see that A beat B by 4–2. But all this information was not needed. We could have had:

(ii)

	Played	Won	Lost	Drawn	Goals for	Goals against
A	1					2
B	1					4

And we would have reached the same conclusion.

Suppose we have three teams, A, B and C, who have
played each other once (so that there are three games).
Then the complete information might be:

(iii)

	Played	Won	Lost	Drawn	Goals for	Goals against
A	2	0	1	1	3	4
B	2	2	0	0	2	0
C	2	0	1	1	3	4

But a lot of this information is not needed. If B scored only 2 goals and won both their two matches, the score in each must have been 1–0. So B v. A and B v. C were both 1–0. And since the third match (A v. C) was drawn and A scored 3 goals, A v. C must have been 3–3 (remember that A scored no goals against B).

Much less information was therefore needed. In fact the following would have been sufficient:

(iv)

	Played	Won	Lost	Drawn	Goals for	Goals against
A					3	
B		2			2	
C				1		

(And this is Puzzle No. 2.)

But in solving this puzzle although it might be helpful to fill up the above diagram, a table that the solver is likely to find more helpful would be this:

(v)

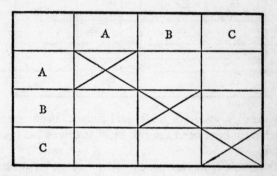

Reading across this gives us the results of A's games against B and against C from A's point of view. And since A did not play A, that square is marked with a cross (as is B v. B and C v. C).

We know that B won both their matches and that the score must therefore have been 1–0 in each. We can fill this up in B's line across. And if B v. A was 1–0, then A v. B was 0–1, etc.

So we have:

(vi)

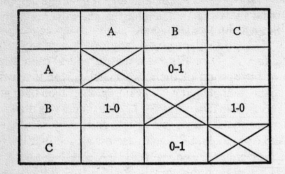

	A	B	C
A	✕	0-1	
B	1-0	✕	1-0
C		0-1	✕

And since A scored 3 goals, and since C drew a match (which must have been against A), A v. C was 3–3 (as was C v. A).

When more teams are concerned it may not be so easy to find a starting-point. A harder (but not really very hard) example may help.

Puzzle No. 77 on page 98.

(vii)

	Played	Won	Lost	Drawn	Goals for	Goals against
A			1	0	1	2
B			1			5
C	2		1		7	4
D		1		0	2	2
E		2		0	5	2

The total of 'goals for' must equal the total of 'goals against' (for each goal appears twice, as a goal for and a goal against).

∴ B's goals for was 0 (to make goals for and goals against both 15). ∴ B (with no goals) cannot have won a match.

Neither A, D or E drew a match, and C cannot have drawn the second of their two matches, for that would make the total of their goals against greater than their goals for (whereas in fact it was 7–4). ∴ no match was drawn. ∴ B can only have played one match, and the score was 0–5.

And if we look at B's goals against we see that B's only match must have been against C. (A and D did not score enough goals and though E scored 5 goals, at least one of them must have been in the other of the two matches which they won.)

∴ B v. C was 0–5, and we know that C's other match was 2–4.

This makes a good starting-point. A diagram like (v) (but for five teams) will now help.

Football, New Method

In this method 10 points are given for a win, 5 points to each side in a match that is drawn, and 1 point for each goal scored. ∴ if A plays B and C, and the scores in those matches were 3–2 and 3–3, then A's points would be: 10 + 5 + 6 (for goals scored), i.e. 21. And B's points (for one game) would be: 0 + 2 (for goals scored), i.e. 2; and C's points would be 5 + 3, i.e. 8.

Let us consider Puzzle No. 24, between three teams – A, B and C.

The total number of points are A, 9; B, 26; C, 7. And we are told that the teams have played each other once. (And that each team has scored at least 1 goal in every match.)

Three matches were played, ∴ 30 points were awarded for wins and draws. ∴ B got 20 points (no team can have got more, for only two matches were played by each team).

∴ A and C each got 5 points for a draw (there is one more match to be played, and this is the only possibility). ∴ numbers of points for goals are: A, 4; B, 6; C, 2. C must have scored 1 goal in each match. ∴ C v. A was 1–1; and C v. B was 1–?. ∴ A got 3 goals in their other match (against B), ∴ A v. B was 3–?.

We know that B won both their matches and scored only 6 goals.

∴ B v. C must have been 2–1

and B v. A must have been 4–3.

The complete solution is   A v. B   3–4;

                          A v. C   1–1;

                          B v. C   2–1.

Letters for Digits

Look at a simple addition sum in which letters have been substituted for digits. The same letter stands for the same digit wherever it appears, and different letters stand for different digits.

Suppose we had:

$$(a)\ (b)\ (c)$$

	R	R
	R	T
X	X	X

122

The most that can be carried when 2 digits are added together is 1. ∴ X = 1.

From (b) R = 5 (5 + 5 = 10, and there must be 1 to carry to make 11).

∴ T = 6 (5 + 6 = 11).

Suppose now that we had:

```
        (a) (b) (c) (d) (e)
         R   R   P   T
         R   T   P   C
        ─────────────────
         X   X   X   T   Z
```

The argument we have already used still applies to:

```
         R  R
         R  T
        ──────
         X  X  X
```

(There cannot be 1 to carry from (d), for if there were T would be 5, but we know that R = 5.)

∴ we know that X = 1, R = 5 and T = 6. And knowing that T = 6, we can see from (d) that P = 3. And since there is nothing to carry from (e) and T = 6, ∴ C must be 2 and Z must be 8. (1 and 3 are X and P.)

∴ Complete solution is:

```
         5 5 3 6
         5 6 3 2
        ─────────
       1 1 1 6 8
```

An important point that arises from this is that the discovery of some letters is likely to make it easier to find out more. The fact that C was 2 and Z was 8 was found to some extent by elimination.

Long Division

There are several different kinds of long division sums in this book. It may be helpful therefore if we say something about:

1 an ordinary long division sum;
2 long division sum with letters substituted for digits;
3 long division sums with most of the figures missing, and in some cases with one of the figures wrong;
4 long division sums with all the figures wrong.

1 Ordinary long division

(i) Let's start with a 'short' division sum. Suppose that we are going to divide 2308 by 3. The work might be set out like this:

$$3 \overline{)2\ 3\ 0\ 8}$$
$$7\ 6\ 9 \quad + \text{a remainder of 1.}$$

In doing this some of the work has been done mentally. We said '3 into 2 will not go; 3 into 23 goes 7 times, and there is a remainder of 2; 3 into 20 goes 6 times and there is a remainder of 2; 3 into 28 goes 9 times and there is a remainder of 1.'

We might have expressed this in more detail by making a long division sum of it thus:

```
          7 6 9
    3 )2 3 0 8
      2 1
      ─────
        2 0
        1 8
        ─────
          2 8
          2 7
          ─────
            1
```

This is just the same as what we did above, except that it is put down in more detail – especially the remainders. The number of times that 3 goes into 2308 is 769, and there is a remainder of 1.

(ii) Let us consider now a long division sum in which we divide by 17.

Thus:

```
            2 3
    1 7 ) 4 0 3
           3 4
          ─────
           6 3
           5 1
          ─────
           1 2
          ─────
```

The method can be seen to be the same as when we were dividing by 3. The result is 23 and there is a remainder of 12.

2 Long division in which letters have been substituted for digits.

Thus:

```
            g b m      (a)
    h g ) h h b g      (b)
          h g          (c)
         ──────
          g b g        (d)
            r m        (e)
         ──────
            g p        (f)
```

In this sum the same letter stands for the same digit wherever it appears. And if we find that, for example, r = 9, then we know that nothing else can be 9.

A starting-point can be got from the fact that (hg) (c) is the same as the divisor, ∴ g (the first digit in (a)) is 1. (We

125

could also have got this from the fact that since (*d*) is a three-figure number, and (*e*) is only a two-figure number, then g = 1.)

From (*b*), (*c*) and (*d*) since g = 1, h = 2 (h − g = g). And since two figures have been brought down in (*d*), b (the second figure in (*a*)) is 0. So we have:

```
            1 0 -        (a)
    2 1 )2 2 0 1         (b)
        2 1              (c)
        ─────
        1 0 1            (d)
          - -            (e)
        ─────
          1 -            (f)
```

21 goes into 101 (*d*) 4 times. ∴ (*e*) is 84 and (*f*) is 17.
∴ r = 8, m = 4 and p = 7.

And complete solution is:

```
            1 0 4
    2 1 )2 2 0 1
        2 1
        ─────
        1 0 1
          8 4
        ─────
          1 7
```

3 Long division sums with most figures missing

(i)

```
            - -          (a)
    - - )- - - 2         (b)
        - 3              (c)
        ─────
          - -            (d)
          - -            (e)
        ─────
          1 -            (f)
```

126

In this long division sum a blank (−) indicates that there is a figure there, but we do not know what it is. We know, for example, that we are dividing a four-figure number ending in 2 (*b*), by a two-figure number. This puzzle (like a lot of the others) is very much easier than it looks at first sight.

When we subtract −3 (*c*) from the first three figures of (*b*) we are left with a single figure (the first figure of (*d*)). Therefore (*b*) must start 10−, and (*c*) must be 93. (If we subtracted 93 from 110, there would be another figure at the beginning of (*d*).) (*e*) cannot be 93, for there could not then be a 1 at the beginning of (*f*).

∴ the divisor is a factor of 93. The only factors of 93 are 31 and 3.

∴ divisor is 31.

(*b*) must start 102 or less, for otherwise there would be another figure in (*d*).

∴ (*d*) must start with 9, 8 or 7. ∴ (*e*) must be 31 times 2, i.e. 62. ∴ (*d*) is 72, (*e*) is 62, and (*f*) is 10.

Complete solution

```
              3 2
      3 1 ) 1 0 0 2
              9 3
              ───
              7 2
              6 2
              ───
              1 0
```

(ii) A long division sum with most of the figures missing and with one of the figures wrong:

```
              7 −        (a)
    − 5 ) − − −          (b)
          − −            (c)
          ───
          − − −          (d)
          − − 8          (e)
```

127

In this long division sum (Puzzle No. 73) you are told that one of the three figures given is wrong. And the question is: 'Which figure is wrong? Find the correct division sum.' In this example it is not possible to point to a certain figure by itself and say 'This one must be wrong.' We must start by trying to find a disagreement between two figures, a situation in which they cannot both be right.

Since the divisor is –5, every multiple of it must end in 0 or in 5. ∴ either the 5 in the divisor or the 8 in (e) must be wrong.

And if the divisor is –5, it must be at least 15. And 15 times 7 (the first figure in (a)) is 105. This has three figures, but (c) has only two. ∴ either the 5 in the divisor or the 7 in (a) must be wrong.

But since we know that only one figure is wrong, it must be the 5 in the divisor. ∴ what we know about the correct sum is:

```
            7 –        (a)
  – – )– – – –          (b)
      – –              (c)
      ───
      – – –            (d)
      – – 8            (e)
```

Readers who have got as far as this would probably like to finish it off themselves. (The solution is on page 199.)

4 Long division sums with all the figures wrong

```
              2 9       (a)
    8 4 )2 2 2 3         (b)
          6 2           (c)
          ───
          6 9 3         (d)
          4 9 3         (e)
```

The above example is Puzzle No. 27. We are told that all the figures are 1 out (i.e. 1 more or 1 less than the correct figures).

With the experience that the reader should now have, a few hints should be enough.

Thus: (*b*) can only start with 1; (*c*) cannot be less than the divisor, ∴ (*c*) must be 73, the divisor is 73, and the first figure in (*a*) is 1. The second figure in (*a*) can only be 8; 8 × 73 = 584; ∴ (*d*) and (*e*) are 584.

Cross Numbers

In a cross-number puzzle it is unlikely that any clue will stand by itself, that is to say can be solved without reference to other clues. If we had a clue, for example: '7 times 9', that would be likely to make the puzzle too easy. We will usually find that each clue has to be considered with one, or perhaps two, or more, others.

Consider Puzzle No. 15 on page 31.

There are no 0's.

Across
1 A perfect square
3 The same when reversed; digits all even
4 Two of the digits are odd; and each one is at least 2 greater than the one before

Down

1 The sum of the digits is 15
2 The digits are all even; each one is greater than the one before
3 A multiple of 7

To find a starting-point may not be immediately easy. But if we look at 2 Down we can see that there are not many alternatives. It must start with either 2 or 4. And if we look at 1 Across ('A perfect square') we see that 2 Down cannot start with 2, for no perfect square ends in 2.

∴ 2 Down can only be 468.

And the only two-figure perfect square ending in 4 is 64. From 3 Across, 3 Down must start with 6, and can only be 63. And the reader will have no difficulty in seeing that 4 Across must be 358, and 1 Down is 645.

Again, as with so many of these puzzles, the difficulty is to find a starting-point. What we need to do is try to find a square where the possibilities are small when we consider the clues in one direction, and are even smaller – preferably only one – when we consider the clues in the other direction.

We have seen that there are only two possibilities for the first digit of 2 Down (2 or 4), and that only one of these (4) can be the second digit of 1 Across.

These considerations enable us to fill in 4 of the 8 squares, and the rest follows fairly easily.

Our Factory

Most of the puzzles about our factory involve finding an order of merit for Alf, Bert, Charlie, etc.

The most important advice to be given for this is to be *orderly* – to set out the alternatives in such a way that it is possible to see, perhaps, that place number 2 could only be filled by one or two of the people concerned.

Let us look at Puzzle No. 11 (a race between five people) on page 28.

We are told that: (i) D was three places above E;
                  (ii) C was not fifth;
                (iii) B's and C's places add up to 8 (there are no ties).

What we know about C, D and E can be set out thus:

1	D	C
2	D	C
3		C
4	E	C
5	E	

And from the fact that B's and C's places add up to 8 we can say, with certainty, that B must be fifth and C must be third (there were no ties, so they cannot both be fourth, and we know that C cannot be fifth).

And since B is fifth, E is not fifth, and we can see from the diagram that E must be fourth (there is no other possibility).

∴ from (i) D is first, ∴ A is second (the only place left).

Cricket

The puzzles about cricket are unlikely to present much difficulty once one sees the fundamental principle that must be used. This principle is best illustrated by giving an example.

Look at Puzzle No. 16 on page 32.

A, B and C have been having a cricket competition in which they have all played against each other once.

131

Points are awarded as follows:

to the side that wins, 10 points;

to the side that wins on the first innings in a drawn match, 6 points;

to the side that loses on the first innings in a drawn match, 2 points;

to each side in a match that is tied, 5 points;

to each side in an uncompleted match, that is tied on the first innings, 4 points;

to the side that loses, 0.

A got 7 points; B got 6 points; and C got 15 points.

Find the result of each match.

What we want to do, if possible, is to find a team that could only have got their points in one way. A got 7 points and there is no way of getting 7 points from two matches (and each team only played two matches) except by tying a match (5 points) and by losing a match on the first innings (2 points). This therefore is what A must have done.

B who got 6 points could not have got 5 points from a tied match for there is no way of getting one point. Therefore A's tied match must have been against C, and the match that A lost on the first innings must have been against B, who therefore got 6 points from it. B therefore got no points in their second match and they lost it against C, who got 10 points.

In some more complicated puzzles there may be one or more alternatives for the number of ways in which teams can have got their points. In this case it may be necessary to try the various possibilities. But we will find that only one of them is acceptable – that is to say fits the whole data of the problem.

Professor Knowall and Serjeant Simple

Puzzles about these two characters can usually be solved by remembering that the same cause has generally the same effect, but the same effect may be preceded by many different causes.

This is seen best in Puzzle No. 42, where the causes and effects are denoted by letters, which make it easier to see how they are related.

As the Professor says in this puzzle to Serjeant Simple: 'If I stand in the rain without any clothes I shall get wet'; and 'But I may also get wet in a lot of other ways, for example, by diving into the sea.'

We are told in this puzzle that there were six possible causes (A, B, C, D, E, F) and that they were followed by four possible defects in a certain machine. We are told that there was every reason to believe that each effect had just one single cause.

The details were as follows:

A, C, F were followed by q and r;
B, C, D, F were followed by s and r;
B, D, E were followed by p and s;
A, D, E, F were followed by p and q.

You are asked to find the causes of p, q, r and s.

What we need to do is to consider what could *not* have caused p. So we want to look at the situations where p is not present on the right.

We see that p is not present on the right in the first two of the four lines above. ∴ p cannot have been caused by A, B, C, D or F. (For if it were, p would have been present when A, B, C, D or F were present.)

∴ p can only be caused by E.

Similarly when we consider q we can see that q was not caused by B, C, D, E or F. ∴ q was caused by A.

And the reader will find it easy now to see that r must have been caused by C, and that s must have been caused by B.

The same principle applies to most of the puzzles about the Professor and the Serjeant.

Solutions

1 Uncle Bungle is Stung by a Couple of Bees ★

$$(a)\ (b)\ (c)$$
$$\text{I}$$
$$\text{B B}$$
$$\overline{\text{I L L}}$$

In column (a) I must be 1 (there can never be more than 1 to carry when two digits are added together).
∴ the letter I = 1.

The first figure in (b) B must be 9, for otherwise there could not be three figures in the answer.
∴ L = 0 (1 + 9 = 10).

Complete solution
$$1$$
$$9\ 9$$
$$\overline{1\ 0\ 0}$$

2 Football ★

Three Teams, Old Method

Consider B. They won two, and scored 2 goals.
∴ B v. A and B v. C were both 1–0.
A scored no goals against B, ∴ all 3 of A's goals were against C.
And since C drew one of their matches, C v. A was 3–3.

Complete solution

A v. B	0–1
A v. C	3–3
B v. C	1–0

3 Multiply by Two ★

If a digit (i.e. a number between 0 and 9) is multiplied by 2, the most that can be carried is 1. $\therefore$ M = 1.
$\therefore$ P = 2 (M × 2);
$\therefore$ A = 4; $\therefore$ X = 7 (7 × 2 = 14).

Complete solution

$$
\begin{array}{r}
7\ 2\ 1 \\
2 \\
\hline
1\ 4\ 4\ 2
\end{array}
$$

4 Addition ★

Letters for Digits, Two Numbers

(a)	(b)	(c)	(d)
F	C	F	
F	C	B	
B	B	J	C

From (*a*) B must be 1, for this is the most that can be carried when two digits are added together. ∴ B = 1.
∴ from (*b*) F = 5. And from (*d*) C = 5 + 1 = 6.
∴ in (*c*) J = 2.

Complete solution

```
  5 6 5
  5 6 1
───────
1 1 2 6
```

5 Competition in Our Factory   ★

B was not first or third, ∴ he was second or fourth, thus:

```
1
2  B
3
4  B
```

D was two places below B.
∴ B must have been second and D fourth, thus:

```
1
2  B
3
4  D
```

And since C was two places above A, C was first and A third.

Complete solution
1   Charlie
2   Bert
3   Alf
4   Duggie

6 Football ★

Three Teams, Old Method

A did not draw any matches, but had as many goals for as
against, ∴ they won one (1–0), and lost one (0–1).
B won both their matches, ∴ A v. B was 0–1, and A v. C
was 1–0.
B scored 5 goals, 1 against A, ∴ 4 against C.
C scored 2 goals, 0 against A, ∴ 2 against B.
∴ B v. C was 4–2.

Complete solution
  A v. B 0–1
  A v. C 1–0
  B v. C 4–2

7 Division ★

Letters for Digits

$$
\begin{array}{r}
\text{d y} \quad (a) \\
\text{d r }\overline{)\text{r r m}} \quad (b) \\
\underline{\text{d r}} \quad (c) \\
\text{d p m} \quad (d) \\
\underline{\text{d p m}} \quad (e) \\
\hline
\end{array}
\qquad
\begin{array}{r}
\text{-- --} \\
\text{-- --}\,\overline{)\text{-- -- --}} \\
\underline{\text{-- --}} \\
\text{-- -- --} \\
\underline{\text{-- -- --}} \\
\hline
\end{array}
$$

(The reader is advised to draw a diagram, like the one on the right above, and to fill in the digits as they are discovered.)

Since (c) is the divisor, the first figure in (a) is 1. $\therefore$ d = 1.

Consider (b), (c) and (d). Since r − r = p, $\therefore$ p = 0.

And since r − d = d (we know that 1 has not been borrowed, and that d = 1), $\therefore$ r = 2. $\therefore$ divisor is 12.

$12 \times 8 = 96$, $\therefore$ to get the three figures in (d) and (e) we must multiply 12 by 9, and we get 108. $\therefore$ m = 8, and y = 9.

Complete solution

```
        1 9
  1 2 )2 2 8
      1 2

      1 0 8
      1 0 8
```

8 Who Pinched My Bike?   ★

Clever's and Loopy's remarks are both false, $\therefore$ neither Loopy nor Clever did it.

'Idle said that Loopy had told him that Noddy did it,' but we know that Loopy was a liar, $\therefore$ Noddy did not do it.
$\therefore$ Idle must have done it.

Complete solution

Idle pinched my bike.

9 Addition ★

Letters for Digits, Two Numbers

$$\begin{array}{ccc} (a) & (b) & (c) \\ P & Y & X \\ P & Y & X \\ \hline Y & Y & P \end{array}$$

Consider (*b*). Remembering that not more than 1 can be carried, Y must be 9. (If Y was 8, we would have $8 + 8 = 7$ (at most), for $8 + 8 = 16$, and $16 + 1 = 17$.) ∴ from (*a*) P = 4, and from (*c*) X = 7. (Remember that 1 is to be carried to (*b*).)

Complete solution

$$\begin{array}{ccc} 4 & 9 & 7 \\ 4 & 9 & 7 \\ \hline 9 & 9 & 4 \end{array}$$

10 A Cross Number ★

1 Down is even.
∴ the first figure of 5 Across is even.
∴ 5 Across must be 258. (Think what would happen if it started with 4.)
∴ 1 Down is 642.
∴ 1 Across is 66.
∴ 2 Down is 685 and 3 Across is 489.

Complete solution

11 Where was Alf? ★

From the facts that D is three places above E and that C is not last, we have as possibilities:

```
1     D  C
2     D  C
3        C
4     E  C
5     E
```

B's and C's places add up to 8. There are no ties. ∴ B must be fifth and C third. And as E cannot be fifth, E is fourth, and D is first. ∴ A is second.

Complete solution
1 Duggie
2 Alf
3 Charlie
4 Ernie
5 Bert

12 Addition ★

Letters for Digits, Two Numbers

$$
\begin{array}{c@{\;}c@{\;}c}
(a) & (b) & (c) \\
X & M & A \\
X & X & A \\
\hline
M & X & X \\
\end{array}
$$

Consider (b). Either M = 0 and there is nothing to carry from (c), or M = 9 and there is 1 to carry from (c).

But it is not possible for the first figure of the answer to be 0, ∴ M = 9. And from (a) X = 4. And since there is 1 to carry from (c), A = 7.

Complete solution

```
4 9 7
4 4 7
─────
9 4 4
```

13 Not as it should be ★

$$
\begin{array}{c@{\;}c@{\;}c}
(a) & (b) & (c) \\
 & 4 & 3 \\
 & 5 & 7 \\
\hline
2 & 0 & 7 \\
\end{array}
$$

When two digits are added together the most that can be carried is 1.

∴ the first figure of the answer is 1; and the second figure of the answer is also 1 (there is nothing else it can be).

Consider (*c*). If both figures (3 and 7) went up to 4 and 8, then the last figure of the answer would be 2, which is not possible. If one (either 3 or 7) went up and the other came down, the last figure of the answer would be 0, which again is not possible. ∴ both figures must come down and must become 2 and 6, and the last figure of the answer must be 8. And there is nothing to carry from (*c*). ∴ the first two figures of (*b*) can only be 5 and 6.

Complete solution

```
  5 2
  6 6
  ‾‾‾
1 1 8
```

14 Football ★

Three Teams, Old Method

B cannot have lost any, for they had no goals against, ∴ they only played one match and they won it (4–0). This match cannot have been against C, for they only had 3 goals against.

∴ B v. A was 4–0, and B did not play C.

∴ C only played A and the score was ?–3.

A had 6 goals against, 4 scored by B and therefore 2 by C.

∴ A v. C was 3–2.

Complete solution

A v. B   0–4
A v. C   3–2

15 A Cross Number ★

Consider 2 Down. The first digit must be 2 or 4. But no perfect square ends in 2.
∴ 1 Across must be 64, and 2 Down must be 468.
∴ the first figure of 3 Across and of 3 Down is 6.
∴ 3 Down is 63.
∴ 4 Across is 358.
∴ 1 Down is 645.

Complete solution

	1 6	2 4
3 6	4	6
4 3	5	8

16 Cricket ★

Three Teams

A	7
B	6
C	15

The only way of getting 7 points from two matches is by tying one (5 points) and by losing one on the first innings (2 points). ∴ this is what A must have done. B, with 6 points, could not have tied one (5 points) for there is no way of getting a single point. ∴ A v. C was a tie (5 points to each). ∴ A's match against B must have been a win for B on the first innings (6 points to B and 2 to A). And the third match (C v. B) was a win for C (10 points to C, no points to B).

Complete solution
A v. B   B won on first innings
A v. C   tie
B v. C   C won

17 Ernie was Odd   ★

'B was twice as many places above A, as D was below C.'
  Suppose D was one place below C, and that B was therefore two places above A. Then we have:

1	B	or	1	C	(if B were second and A
2			2	D	fourth, D and C cannot be
3	A		3	B	one place apart)
4	C		4		
5	D		5	A	

And E would be second or fourth – but neither of these is odd. ∴ D must be two places below C, and B must be four places above A. And we have:

1	B
2	C
3	
4	D
5	A

∴ E must be third.

Complete solution
1 Bert
2 Charlie
3 Ernie
4 Duggie
5 Alf

18 Division ★

Some Missing Figures

```
                    – 1      (a)
        4 – )– – – 9          (b)
                 – –          (c)
              ———————
                 – –          (d)
                 – –          (e)
              ———————
```

Since the sum comes out exactly, the second figures of (*d*) and (*e*) are both 9.

And since (*e*) is the divisor multiplied by 1, the divisor must be 49. ∴ the first figure in (*a*) must be 2 and (*c*) must be 98. (The first figure in (*a*) cannot be more than 2, for (*c*) would then have three figures.)

Add up from the bottom and we get:

Complete solution

```
          2 1
49 ) 1 0 2 9
      9 8
        4 9
        4 9
```

19 Cricket ★

Three Teams

A's points can either be (10 + 2) or (6 + 6).
Suppose A's points were 6 + 6. Then A v. B was a win on first innings for A, ∴ B got 2 points. ∴ B (who got 10 points) got 8 points for their other match.

But there is no way of getting 8 points for a match.
∴ A's points must have been (10 + 2).
∴ Either B or C must have got 6 points against A. But not C, who only got 4 points.
∴ B beat A on first innings.
∴ A v. C was a win for A.
∴ B v. C was a tie on first innings (they both got 4 points).

Complete solution

   A v. B   B won on first innings
   A v. C   A won
   B v. C   tie on first innings

20 Division ★

Letters for Digits

```
            z e p    (a)                   - - -
    p d ) y x q x z  (b)          - - ) - - - - -
          d b        (c)                   - -
          ─────
          p y x      (d)                 - - -
          z h s      (e)                 - - -
          ─────
          y b z      (f)                 - - -
          y y y      (g)                 - - -
          ─────
            p y      (h)                   - -
          ─────
```

(The reader is advised to draw a figure like the one on the
right above, and to fill in the digits there as they are
discovered.)

From (*b*) y = 1; ∴ from (*f*), (*g*) and (*h*) z = 2; ∴ from (*d*)
and (*e*) p = 3. ∴ from (*f*), (*g*) and (*h*) b = 4. From (*g*)
divisor is $\frac{111}{3}$ = 37; ∴ d = 7. From (*b*), (*c*) and (*d*)
q = 5, and x = 0. ∴ from (*d*), (*e*) and (*f*) s = 6, and h = 9;
∴ in (*a*) e = 8.

Complete solution

```
            2 8 3
    3 7 ) 1 0 5 0 2
          7 4
          ___
          3 1 0
          2 9 6
          ___
            1 4 2
            1 1 1
            ___
              3 1
```

21 Stealing, Breaking and Stopping ★

Denote window breaking by p; clock stopping by q; and pencil stealing by r.

Then we have:

$$A, C, D \rightarrow p, q \quad (a)$$
$$A, B, C \rightarrow r, p \quad (b)$$
$$A, D \rightarrow q \quad (c)$$

In order to find who was responsible for r it will be best to find out who was there when there was no r, for we know that if the pencil stealer is there he will steal pencils. When there is no r, those present are A, C, and D.

∴ B is responsible for r.

Similarly from (c) p is not caused by A, D, but by B or C. But C is present in (a) and (b) (when p appears) and B is not.

∴ C is responsible for p.

Similarly from (b) q is not caused by A, B, C.

∴ D is responsible for q.

Complete solution
　Bert was the pencil stealer;
　Charlie was the window breaker;
　Duggie was the clock stopper.

22 Only One Out　　　　　　★

(a)	(b)	(c)	(d)	(e)	(f)
2	1	6	6	4	8
	9	0	1	3	5
1	3	7	8	0	

Consider (*f*). 0 must be 1, ∴ 8 must be 7 and 5 must be 6 to make the difference 1. ∴ we have:

$$\begin{array}{r} 7 \\ 6 \\ \hline 1 \\ \hline \end{array}$$

Consider (*e*). This must be:

$$\begin{array}{r} 3 \\ 4 \\ \hline 9 \\ \hline \end{array}$$

(If the figure on the first line is 5, and on the second line 2, the difference would only be 3, but it must be at least 7.)

　Consider (*d*). Remember that 1 has been borrowed, so that difference is now 4. We must make them farther apart, thus:

$$
\begin{array}{r}
7 \\
0 \\
\hline
6 \\
\hline
\end{array}
$$

Consider (*c*). 0 can only be 1, ∴ we must have:

$$
\begin{array}{r}
5 \\
1 \\
\hline
4 \\
\hline
\end{array}
$$

Consider (*b*). 1 in the answer can only be 2 (it would not make sense to have 0 at the beginning of the answer). And 9 cannot go up, so it must be 8. ∴ we have:

$$
\begin{array}{r}
0 \\
8 \\
\hline
2 \\
\hline
\end{array}
$$

And (*a*) must be 1.

Complete solution

$$
\begin{array}{r}
1\ 0\ 5\ 7\ 3\ 7 \\
8\ 1\ 0\ 4\ 6 \\
\hline
2\ 4\ 6\ 9\ 1 \\
\hline
\end{array}
$$

23 Addition ★

Letters for Digits, Three Numbers

	(a)	(b)	(c)
	R	A	X
	A	A	X
	X	A	X
	M	P	M

Consider (*a*). Since there are no 1's, and R, A and X are all different, they must be at least 2, 3 and 4. But 2 + 3 + 4 = 9.
∴ M must be 9, and R, A and X must be 2, 3 and 4, though we do not yet know which is which.

Since M = 9, from (*c*) X must be 3.

Consider (*b*). A cannot be 4, for 4 + 4 + 4 = 12 and there would be 1 to carry. But we know there is not.
∴ A = 2; ∴ R = 4; and P = 6.

Complete solution

```
  4 2 3
  2 2 3
  3 2 3
  ─────
  9 6 9
```

24 Football ★

Three Teams, New Method

A cannot have got more than 5 points for wins or draws.
C cannot have got more than 5 points for wins or draws.
B cannot have got more than 20 points for wins and draws
for they can only have played two matches.
∴ A got 5 points for wins or draws, and 4 points for goals.
  B got 20 points for wins or draws and 6 points for goals.
  C got 5 points for wins or draws and 2 points for goals.
B must have won against A and against C, and C v. A must
have been a draw.
∴ C v. A was 1–1, and C v. B was 1–?.
A got 4 goals, ∴ A v. B was 3–?.
B got 6 goals, ∴ B v. C was 2–1, and B v. A was 4–3.
(The only possibilities since B won both matches.)

Complete solution
  A v. B   3–4
  A v. C   1–1
  B v. C   2–1

25 Football ★

Four Teams, Old Method

D played everyone, but A and B only played D, ∴. C can
only have played D (there is no one else for them to play).
∴. C v. D was 2–2.
  Since B got 2 points, B beat D, and since D got 3 points,
D beat A.

155

Since A only had 1 goal scored against them, D v. A was 1–0.

D got 4 goals, 2 against C, 1 against A, so they must have scored 1 against B. And since B got 3 goals, B v. D was 3–1.

Complete solution

    A v. D   0–1
    B v. D   3–1
    C v. D   2–2

26 Who Does What in Our Factory ★

With a diagram this becomes a very simple problem. Thus:

	D-Op	D-Sh	D-K-P	B-W	W O	S-U	Worker
A				X			X
B	X		X	X			X
C							
D	X	X		X	X		X
E							
F	X		X				X
G							

Information about A, F, B and D has been inserted in diagram. The reader is advised to insert information about D-Sh, S-U, etc., in his own diagram.

It will then be seen that E must be the Worker; ∴ no one else can be. Fill in this information and it will be seen that A is D-K-P. And then, in succession, C is D-O; F is D-Sh; G is B-W; B is W O; D is S-U.

Complete solution

    Alf is the Door-Knob-Polisher;
    Bert is the Welfare Officer;
    Charlie is the Door-Opener;
    Duggie is the Sweeper-Upper;
    Ernie is the Worker;
    Fred is the Door-Shutter;
    George is the Bottle-Washer.

27 Uncle Bungle Shows that ★ He Can Get Division Sums Wrong Too!

```
              2 9      (a)
     8 4 ) 2 2 2 3     (b)
           6 2         (c)
           ─────
           6 9 3       (d)
           4 9 3       (e)
           ─────
```

Remember that all figures are 1 out. The first figure of (*a*) must be 1 or 3; and the first figure in the divisor must be 7 or 9. ∴ (*c*) cannot be the divisor multiplied by 3 (it would have to have three figures). ∴ the first digit in (*a*) is 1. And the divisor is 7–.

The second figure in the divisor is 1 more or less than 2, and 1 more or less than 4. ∴ the divisor is 73.

The second figure in (*a*) can only be 8, ∴ (*d*) and (*e*) are 73 × 8, i.e. 584.

Add up from the bottom and we get:

Complete solution

```
            1 8
    7 3 )1 3 1 4
          7 3
        ───────
          5 8 4
          5 8 4
        ───────
```

28 Addition ★

Letters for Digits, Two Numbers

```
    (a) (b) (c) (d) (e)
        R   P   A   P
        A   B   B   M
      ─────────────────
      R   R   R   R   P
```

The most that can be carried when adding two digits is 1, ∴ the first R in the answer is 1, ∴ all the other R's are 1.

Consider (*e*). P + M = P, ∴ M = 0 (but we cannot yet say what P is). Note that there is nothing to carry.

From (*b*) R + A + (perhaps) 1 = 11. ∴ A must be 9, and there is 1 carried from (*c*).
We know that A + B = 11. ∴ B = 2.
And P + B + 1 = 11, ∴ P = 8.

Complete solution

```
  1 8 9 8
  9 2 2 0
  ───────
1 1 1 1 8
```

29 Football ★

Three Teams, New Method

3 matches were played, ∴ 30 points were given for wins and draws.
C cannot have got more than 5 points for wins or draws, ∴ C scored 3 goals.
B cannot have got more than 10 points for wins or draws, ∴ B scored 5 goals.
And A cannot have got more than 15 points for wins or draws, ∴ A scored 7 goals.

Since B did not lose a match, both their matches were draws and A won the third match against C.

C only scored 3 goals, so we have:

	A	B	C
A	✕	dr.	w. ?-1 ?-2
B	dr.	✕	dr. 2-2 1-1
C	L. 1-? 2-?	dr. 2-2 1-1	✕

If B v. C was 1–1, then B v. A would be 4–4, – but not more than 7 goals were scored in any match.

∴ B v. C was 2–2, and B v. A was 3–3.

∴ A scored 4 goals against C (7 altogether), ∴ A v. C was 4–1.

Complete solution

  A v. B   3–3
  A v. C   4–1
  B v. C   2–2

30 The Good Worker ★

G says that F is the Worker. This cannot be true, for there would then be two people who have told the truth, G and the Worker (F). ∴ G's statement is false, and F is *not* the Worker.

∴ E is the Worker.

And since E's statement is true, G is the Door-Shutter.

∴ F must be the Door-Opener.

Complete solution
Ernie is the Worker;
Fred is the Door-Opener;
George is the Door-Shutter.

31 Still Only One Out ★

	(a)	(b)	(c)	(d)
	2	9	1	0
	1	4	9	7
	2	1	0	6

Consider (d). 0 must be 1; ∴ the other two figures must add up to 11. ∴ 7 must be 6 and 6 must be 5.

Consider (c). 0 must be 1. And 9 must be 8. ∴ 1 must be 0 (remember that there was 1 to borrow).

Consider (b). 9 must be 8. And remembering that there was 1 to borrow, 4 must be 5 and 1 must be 2.

Consider (a). 1 must be 2 (we cannot have 0 at the beginning of the line). ∴ the first 2 must be 3 (it must be more than 2). ∴ the second 2 is 1.

Complete solution

3	8	0	1
2	5	8	6
1	2	1	5

32 Football ★

Four Teams, New Method

Neither B nor C can have got any points for wins or draws.
A can only have got 15 (out of their 20), and D can only
have got 25 (out of their 30).

But $15 + 25 = 40$, and this is the number of points for
wins or draws for four games.

D with 25 points for wins or draws must have won 2 and
drawn 1, ∴ they played everybody, including C.

But C, with 1 point, only played one match, ∴ C v. A and
C v. B were the matches that have not been played.

D's drawn match must have been against A (B and C won
none and drew none), and D beat B and C.

Since D only scored 5 goals, D v. B was 2–1, D v. C was
2–1, and D v. A was 1–1.

A only scored 1 goal against D, ∴ A scored 4 goals
against B.

B only scored 1 goal against D, ∴ B scored 3 goals
against A. ∴ A v. B was 4–3.

Complete solution

    A v. B   4–3
    A v. D   1–1
    B v. D   1–2
    C v. D   1–2

33 Who was X?   ★

E was as many places before C as G was before A, ∴ C and
A were not first and E and G were not fourth.
Also E was not first and A was not second.
∴ since A, C and E were not first, G was first.
∴ A cannot be fourth (G would then be three places before
A and E would only be one place before C).
∴ C was fourth (no one else can be).
∴ E was second (two places before C)
and A was third (two places after G).

Complete solution
   1   George
   2   Ernie
   3   Alf
   4   Charlie
       Charlie was X.

34 Cricket   ★

Three Teams

Each team played two matches.

   A can only have got 11 points by drawing one (5) and
winning one on first innings (6).

   The only way in which C can have got 7 points is by
drawing one (5) and losing one on first innings (2).

   Suppose that A v. C was a draw. Then A's other match
was against B and since A got 6 points, B got 2. C's other
match was against B, and since C got 2 points, B got 6. But

B's points are 10, not $2 + 6$. ∴ A v. C was not a draw, ∴ A's drawn match was against B, and C's drawn match was against B (making B's points 10).

And A v. C was a win on first innings for A.

Complete solution

A v. B   tie

A v. C   A won on first innings

B v. C   tie

35 Division ★

Some Missing Figures

$$
\begin{array}{r}
- \ 5 \ - \quad (a) \\
- - \overline{)6 - - -} \quad (b) \\
- - \quad (c) \\
\hline
- - - \quad (d) \\
- - \quad (e) \\
\hline
- \ 7 \ - \quad (f) \\
- - - \quad (g) \\
\hline
\end{array}
$$

(*e*) is the divisor times 5. But since (*e*) only has two figures the divisor must be less than 20. From (*f*) –7– is a multiple of the divisor but 18×9 is only 162, ∴ the divisor must be 19, and (*f*) and (*g*) are 171.

Since (*d*) has three figures and (*e*) has two, (*e*) must be the two-figure multiple of 19 nearest to 100, i.e. 95 (19×5). (*d*) starts with 1, ∴ the first figure of (*c*) must be 4 or 5. But it cannot be 4, for there is no two-figure multiple of 19 starting with 4. ∴ (*c*) is 57 (19×3).

Add up from the bottom and we get:

Complete solution

```
        3 5 9
  1 9 ) 6 8 2 1
      5 7
      1 1 2
        9 5
      1 7 1
      1 7 1
```

36 Addition   ★

Letters for Digits, Two Numbers

$$
\begin{array}{ccc}
(a) & (b) & (c) \\
Z & B & B \\
B & Y & B \\
\hline
C & Z & Z
\end{array}
$$

Consider (b) *and* (c). If B were less than 5, then there would be nothing to carry from (c) to (b) and Y would be equal to B. But this is not possible. ∴ B is greater than 5.

Suppose B = 6, then Z = 2, and (a) is 2 + 6, so that C is 8 or 9.

If B were 7, then Z would be 4 and Z + B would be greater than 9.

∴ B = 6, Z = 2, Y = 5, C = 9.

Complete solution

```
  2 6 6
  6 5 6
 ──────
  9 2 2
```

37 The Running-Backward ★ Race

Suppose E was second. Then D would have to be first. But if B was third, A and C would have to be fourth and fifth, so that the difference between D and B would not be the same as the difference between A and C.

It can similarly be seen that it is not possible for E to be fourth and, as E was not first or third, E can only be fifth.

B was not second, ∴ D must have been first, A second, B third and C fourth.

Complete solution

1 Duggie
2 Alf
3 Bert
4 Charlie
5 Ernie

38 Football ★★

Four Teams, Old Method

Consider D. They lost none and drew none; but their goals for were only 1 more than their goals against, ∴ they can only have played one match, which must have been against C (who played everyone) and the score was 2–1.

Consider A. They won none and drew one, and had the same number of goals for as against.

∴ they cannot have lost any, for, if they had, their goals against would have been more than their goals for.

∴ they only played one, which must have been against C, and the score was 3–3.

∴ B can only have played one match, against C (there is no one else for them to play).

And C v. B was 3–0 ((7 − 3 − 1) − (5 − 3 − 2))

Complete solution

    A v. C   3–3
    B v. C   0–3
    C v. D   1–2

39 Addition ★★

Letters for Digits, Two Numbers

$$
\begin{array}{c c c c}
R & A & A & P \\
G & G & A & P \\
\hline
P \quad M & B & M & R
\end{array}
$$

The most that can be carried when two digits are added together is 1. $\therefore$ P = 1.

$\therefore$ R = P + P = 2.

Suppose G = 9, then 9 + 2 (plus, perhaps, 1 which has been carried) cannot be more than 12. But M cannot be 1 or 2, for P = 1, and R = 2.

$\therefore$ M must be 0.

$\therefore$ A + A = 10, and A = 5.

$\therefore$ there is 1 to carry from A + G (for G is at least 7).

$\therefore$ G = 7 (2 + 7 + 1 = 10) and B = 3.

Complete solution

```
    2 5 5 1
    7 7 5 1
  ─────────
  1 0 3 0 2
```

40 All is Confusion – but the   ★★ Bottle-Washer was Third

(i)   The Bottle-Washer was third.

(ii)   From (2) the Worker was fifth (no one else can be).

(iii) $\therefore$ from (1) the Door-Opener was fourth, and B was first.

(iv)   From (3) C was fifth (not A from (1), not (D) from (4) since the Door-Shutter was first or second, and not E from (5)). $\therefore$ the Door-Knob-Polisher was second.

(v) $\therefore$ the Door-Shutter was first (no one else can be). $\therefore$ from (4), D was second.

(vi) $\therefore$ from (5), E was fourth and A was third.

Complete solution

1. Bert (Door-Shutter)
2. Duggie (Door-Knob-Polisher)
3. Alf (Bottle-Washer)
4. Ernie (Door-Opener)
5. Charlie (Worker)

41 Multiply by 4 ★★

$$\begin{array}{cccc} C & B & D & F \quad (a) \\ & & & 4 \\ \hline D & F & D & E \quad D \quad (b) \end{array}$$

D, the last digit of (b), must be even, since (a) has been multiplied by 4. But D, the first digit of (b), cannot be more than 3 (9999 × 4 starts with 3), and since D is even, D = 2.

F could be 3 or 8 (4 × 3 = 12, 4× 8 = 32). Suppose F = 8, then there is 3 to carry and E = 1 (8 + 3 = 11), and the third figure in (b), D, would be odd. But D = 2. ∴ F cannot be 8, ∴ F = 3. And E = (4 × 2) + 1 = 9.

The first two figures of (b) are 23, ∴ C = 5, and there must have been 3 to carry. ∴ B = 8.

Complete solution

$$\begin{array}{ccccc} & 5 & 8 & 2 & 3 \\ & & & & 4 \\ \hline 2 & 3 & 2 & 9 & 2 \end{array}$$

42 Cause and Effect ★★

We have: A, C, F   →   q, r   (*a*)

        B, C, D, F   →   s, r   (*b*)

        B, D, E   →   p, s   (*c*)

        A, D, E, F   →   p, q   (*d*)

Consider p: from (*a*) and (*b*), p is *not* caused by A, B, C, D, F.

∴ p is caused by E.

   Consider q: from (*b*) and (*c*), q is *not* caused by B, C, D, E, F.

∴ q is caused by A.

   Consider r: from (*c*) and (*d*), r is *not* caused by A, B, D, E, F.

∴ r is caused by C.

   Consider s: from (*a*) and (*d*), s is *not* caused by A, C, D, E, F.

∴ s is caused by B.

Complete solution

   p is caused by E

   q is caused by A

   r is caused by C

   s is caused by B

43 Two, Four, Six, Eight ★★

```
                2 -      (a)
        4 - )- - - 8     (b)
              - - -      (c)
              ─────
               - -       (d)
               6 -       (e)
               ───
```

Look first for figure that is wrong. $49 \times 2 = 98$; ∴ either 4 or 2 is wrong. And either 4 or 6 is wrong, for $4- \times 1$ is $4-$, and $4- \times 2$ would be at least $8-$.

∴ as only one figure is wrong, it must be 4.

∴ as (c) (three figures) is divisor times 2, (d) and (e) must be the divisor.

∴ the divisor is 68, and the second figure in (a) is 1.

∴ (c) (divisor times 2) = 136.

Add up from the bottom and we get:

Complete solution

The figure 4 was wrong.

```
              2 1
      6 8 )1 4 2 8
          1 3 6
          ─────
            6 8
            6 8
            ───
```

171

44 Football ★★

Three Teams, Old Method

Since the total of goals against must be the same as the total of goals for, B have 5 goals scored against them.

A and B scored 7 goals (5 + 2) and C had 4 goals scored against them.

∴ A and B must have scored 3 goals (7 − 4) in their match against each other.

∴ A v. B could not have been a draw.

∴ B v. C was the drawn match.

And since B has 2 goals for and 5 goals against, B lost their other match (against A) by 3 goals. And since 'A and B must have scored 3 goals in their match against each other' (see above), A v. B was 3–0; ∴ A v. C was 2–4 and B v. C was 2–2.

Complete solution
    A v. B   3–0
    A v. C   2–4
    B v. C   2–2

45 A Cross Number ★★

3 Across and 4 Down are both perfect squares. And from 5 Across, 4 Down is even.

∴ 4 Down must be 16, 36 or 64. ∴ 3 Across must be 81, 36 or 16.

But not 81 (see 2 Down and 5 Across; last digit of 2 Down must be at least 8).

And not 16 (see 2 Down).

∴ 3 Across is 36, and 4 Down is 64.

1 Across must be 12 (not 18, see 2 Down). The third digit of 2 Down must be 4, 6 or 8, but not 4 or 8 (see 5 Across), ∴ it is 6.

∴ 5 Across is 264.

And 1 Down is 192.

Complete solution

1	2	
1	2	/////
9	3 3	4 6
5 2	6	4

46 A Competition ★★

Since neither C nor E was third or fifth, we have:

1
2
3 A, B, D
4
5 A, B, D

But A was above B, ∴ A was not fifth, and D is above E, ∴ D was not fifth.

∴ B was fifth.

∴ either A or D was third.

  Suppose D was third; then E was fourth, so that D was

one place above E. But it is not possible for A to be one place above B. ∴ D was not third.

∴ A was third.

And since A was two places above B, D was two places above E.

∴ D was second, E was fourth and C was first.

Complete solution
1   Charlie
2   Duggie
3   Alf
4   Ernie
5   Bert

47 Division ★★

Figures All Wrong

$$
\begin{array}{r}
3\ 8 \quad (a) \\
2\ 3\ \overline{)8\ 7\ 5} \quad (b) \\
7\ 7 \quad (c) \\
\hline
2\ 1\ 5 \quad (d) \\
4\ 1\ 5 \quad (e) \\
\hline
\end{array}
$$

(d) and (e) must both be the same. And since the figures are only 1 out, (d) and (e) must both be 3—.

Divisor starts with 1 or 3. If 1, the most it can be is 14. And (d) and (e) cannot then be more than $14 \times 9 = 126$.

∴ the divisor cannot start with 1, but must start with 3. If the divisor were 32 then (d) and (e) could not be more than $32 \times 9 = 288$.

∴ the divisor must be 34, not 32. And the second figure in (*a*) must be 9 (for 34 × 7 is only 238).

∴ (*d*) and (*e*) are 306.

If the first figure in (*a*) were 4 then (*c*) would have three figures (34 × 4 = 136).

∴ the first figure in (*a*) is 2, and (*c*) is 68.

Add up from the bottom and we get:

Complete solution

```
          2 9
   3 4 ) 9 8 6
          6 8
        ─────
        3 0 6
        3 0 6
        ─────
```

48 Football   ★★

Three Teams, New Method

The points are: A – 8
B – 14
C – 9

The greatest number of points that they can get for wins or draws is: A – 5, B – 10, C – 5. ∴ only two matches were played (not one, for in that case one of them would have got *no* points).

Suppose that B drew two matches, against A and C, then B's total of goals should equal (A + C)'s total. But B's total is 4, and A's is 3 and C's is 4.

∴ A v. C was a draw and B won one.

Either A or C played only one game, and since A got 3 goals and C got 4, A v. C must have been 3–3. And C scored 1 goal against B.
∴ B v. C was 4–1.

Complete solution
    A v. C   3–3
    B v. C   4–1

49 Serjeant Simple Loses ★★
his Wallet

Remember that from 'If p, then q' it does not follow that 'If q, then p'. (For example, from 'If that animal is a cow, then it has four legs' it does *not* follow that 'If that animal has four legs, then it is a cow'.)

But from 'If p, then q', 'If *not* q, then *not* p' does follow. (Using the same example, 'If that animal has *not* got four legs, then it is *not* a cow'.)

(1) is equivalent to: 'If you find your wallet it is because you have not looked in the deep freeze.' That is, 'If you look in the deep freeze you will *not* find your wallet.'

(2) is equivalent to: 'If you look behind the desk you will find your wallet.'

(3) is in the form 'Not both p and q', from which we can deduce 'If p then *not* q.' ∴ it is equivalent to 'If you look in the cycle shed you will *not* find your wallet.'

Complete solution
Serjeant Simple's wallet is behind the desk.

50 A Cross Number ★★

Consider 4 Down. Perfect squares of two figures starting with an odd number (see 3 Across) are 16 and 36. But from 3 Across 4 Down must be 36, and 3 Across must be 123.

The only factors of 3 Across (123) are 3 and 41.

∴ 1 Across must be 41.

5 Across is 41–(1 Down) multiplied by an even number, ∴ it must be 41 × 2, and since 5 Across ends in 6, 1 Down is 418 and 5 Across is 836.

Complete solution

1 4	2 1	////
3 1	2	4 3
5 8	3	6

51 The Factory Dinner-Party ★★

Since C does not have A on his right, C must have E on his right (not B or D), and A on his left.

B cannot be next to A, ∴ D is on A's left and B is between D and E.

Thus:

B is between W O and D-S, and B is between E and D; ∴ D is either the W O or D-S, and we are also told that either the D-S or the D-O is D.

∴ D must be D-S. ∴ E is W O. And since the D-O and D-S are not next to each other, C is D-O. A is not B-W, ∴ B is B-W, and A is the Worker.

Complete solution

52 Division ★★

Letters for Digits

```
        d k g b        (a)              - - - -
d h ) g d n s f s      (b)        - - )- - - - - -
      g g n            (c)              - - -
      ─────
        s f s          (d)              - - -
        g h k          (e)              - - -
      ─────
          n f          (f)                - -
          d h          (g)                - -
        ─────
          d g s        (h)              - - -
          d g s        (i)              - - -
        ─────
```

(The reader is advised to draw a figure like the one on the right above, where the digits can be inserted as they are found.)

Consider the third figures of (b) and (c); n − n is f; ∴ f = 0. In (g), dh is the divisor; ∴ the third figure in (a) is 1, i.e. g = 1.

Since g = 1, from (d) and (e), s = 2.

From (b), (c) and (d) d − 1 = 2, ∴ d = 3.

From (f), (g) and (h) h = 9 and n = 7.

From (d), (e) and (f) k = 5. And b is 312 divided by 39, i.e. b = 8.

Complete solution

```
            3 5 1 8
      39 ) 1 3 7 2 0 2
          1 1 7
          ─────
            2 0 2
            1 9 5
            ─────
              7 0
              3 9
              ───
              3 1 2
              3 1 2
```

53 A Cross Number ★★

1 Down is a perfect square, and from 4 Across it must be the square of an odd number. ∴ it must be the square of 5, 7 or 9. But not 7, for 4 Across would then be 9–9, and this is not possible (see 3 Down). And not 9, for 4 Across would then be 1–1, and this is not possible (see 3 Down). ∴ 1 Down is 25. And 1 Across can only be 234 (see 3 Down and 4 Across).

The last figure of 3 Down is 6, 7, 8 or 9. But not 7 or 8 for 5 Across is a perfect square. And not 6, for 5 Across would then be 16, and the sum of the digits of 2 Down could not be 16. ∴ 5 Across must be 49; and 2 Down must be 394.

¹ 2	² 3	³ 4
⁴ 5	9	5
//////	⁵ 4	9

54 Letters for Digits ★★

A Multiplication

$$
\begin{array}{cccccc}
(a) & (b) & (c) & (d) & (e) & (f) \\
P & M & M & T & & P \\
 & & & & & P \\
\hline
N & P & T & R & P & T
\end{array}
$$

Since P = 2T, P is even. And from (*f*), P times P ends in T (half of P). ∴ P cannot be 2 (2 × 2 = 4); nor 4 (4 × 4 ends in 6); nor 6 (6 × 6 ends in 6). But 8 × 8 ends in 4 (half of 8), ∴ P = 8, and T = 4.

In (*b*) P = 8, ∴ the first figure of the answer is 6 (8 × 8 = 64). ∴ N = 6.

Consider (*c*). 8 × M must be large enough for 4 to be carried (so that, in (*a*) and (*b*), 64 will become 68). ∴ M must be 5 or 6 (8 × 5 = 40, and 8 × 6 = 48). But it cannot be 6, for N = 6; ∴ M = 5.

We now know the whole of the first line. Multiply by 8, and we get the answer.

Complete solution

```
  8 5 5 4 8
          8
───────────
6 8 4 3 8 4
```

55 Uncle Bungle's Football Puzzle ★★

	Played	Won	Lost	Drawn	Goals for	Goals against
A		2			2	
B			0	0	4	3
C					5	3
D	3					

Consider B. They lost none and drew none, ∴ they won all their matches. But they scored only one goal more than the goals scored against them, so they can only have won one, and ∴ only played one. D played all the other three, ∴ B v. D was 4–3.

Consider A. They won two and scored 2 goals, ∴ the score in each match that they won was 1–0, and they did not play B, for B only played D. So we have:

	A	B	C	D
A			1-0	1-0
B				4-3
C	0-1			
D	0-1	3-4		

And since D played three matches, D played C.
C v. A was 0–1, and C's total goals for and against were 5–3.
∴ C v. D was 5–2.

Complete solution
    A v. C   1–0
    A v. D   1–0
    B v. D   4–3
    C v. D   5–2

56 Addition ★★

Letters for Digits, Two Numbers

$$
\begin{array}{cccccc}
(a) & (b) & (c) & (d) & (e) & (f) \\
R & X & E & K & P & P \\
R & X & X & R & P & P \\
\hline
H & R & B & H & P & H \\
\end{array}
$$

Consider (*e*). P must be 0 (0 + 0 = 0); or 9 (9 + 9 = 18, and 1 might be carried to make 19).

But if P were 0, then the last figure in the answer (H) should also be 0. ∴ P = 9, and H = 8.

∴ in (*a*) R = 4.

And in (*b*) X = 2; and in (*d*) K = 3. In (*c*) E + 2 = B.

∴ E = 5 and B = 7 (the only figures differing by 2 that are left).

Complete solution

```
  4 2 5 3 9 9
  4 2 2 4 9 9
  ───────────
  8 4 7 8 9 8
```

57 Cricket ★★

Three Teams

There is no way of getting 3 points, ∴ *A's figure is wrong.*

Each side played two matches, and there is no way of getting 13 points from two matches.

∴ C's figure is wrong.

∴ B's figure is correct.

The only way in which B can get 11 points is by tying one match (5 points) and by winning one on the first innings (6). Suppose B v. A was a tie; then A get 5 points from their match against B. And A must get at least 2 points from their match against C, making 7 points. But we know that A's incorrect figure of 3 is not more than 2 out. ∴ B v. A was not a tie.

∴ B v. C was a tie and B beat A on the first innings.

∴ A got 2 points from their match against B, and must also have got 2 points from their match against C (making 4 points).

And C got 6 (against A) and 5 (against B) making 11 points.

Complete solution

A v. B   B won on first innings
A v. C   C won on first innings
B v. C   tie

58 Division   ★★

Figures All Wrong

$$\begin{array}{r}
3\ 4 \quad (a) \\
1\ 4\ )\overline{6\ 1\ 8} \quad (b) \\
\underline{5\ 5} \quad (c) \\
\\
7\ 8 \quad (d) \\
\underline{5\ 8} \quad (e)
\end{array}$$

Since each digit is only 1 out the divisor must start with 2 (it cannot start with 0).

Since the sum comes out exactly, (d) and (e) must be the same. ∴ they must both start with 6.

∴ the second figure in (a) must be 3 (it cannot be 5 for 2–times 5 is 100 or more).

If the second figure in the divisor was 5 then (d) and (e) would be 75, but they both start with 6. ∴ the divisor must be 23, and (d) and (e) must be 69.

The first figure in (a) cannot be 4, for (c) would then be

185

92, which it cannot be. ∴ the first figure in (*a*) is 2, and (*c*) is 46.

Add up from the bottom and we get:

Complete solution

```
        2 3
   2 3 ) 5 2 9
         4 6
         ───
         6 9
         6 9
         ───
```

59 Football

Four Teams, Old Method

Consider C. 1 goal for and 1 goal against, but no drawn matches.

∴ C can only have played two, and won one (1–0) and lost the other (0–1).

And C cannot have played D, who played only one match but had 3 goals against in this match. ∴ C played A and B.

And since A drew 2, they played all the other three, and their match against D must have been drawn, with a score of 3–3. (Remember that D only played one match, and had 3 goals against.)

B did not play D, but they drew against A and they lost a match.

∴ B v. C was 0–1; ∴ A v. C was 1–0.

B scored 4 goals, ∴ B v. A was 4–4.

Complete solution

A v. B	4–4	
A v. C	1–0	
A v. D	3–3	
B v. C	0–1	

60 Multiply by 3 ★★

$$
\begin{array}{cccccc}
(a) & (b) & (c) & (d) & (e) & (f) \\
L & D & C & F & L \\
& & & & & 3 \\
\hline
H & J & D & H & H & L
\end{array}
$$

Consider (f). L × 3 produces a number ending in L. ∴ L must be 0 or 5. But it cannot be 0, for in (b) L cannot be 0. ∴ L = 5.

∴ 3 × L = 15, ∴ the first figure of the answer must be 1. ∴ H = 1.

∴ in (e) H is 1, and since 1 has been carried from (f) (3 × 5 = 15), F = 0. And there is nothing to carry to (d). ∴ C = 7 (3 × 7 = 21) and there is 2 to carry.

(3 × D) + 2 produces D, ∴ D could be 4 (3 × 4 = 12, and 2 makes 14), or D could be 9 (3 × 9 = 27, and 2 makes 29).

But if D were 9, then J would be (5 + 2), i.e. 7. But we know that C = 7. ∴ D = 4 and J = 6.

Complete solution

$$
\begin{array}{ccccc}
5 & 4 & 7 & 0 & 5 \\
& & & & 3 \\
\hline
1\;6 & 4 & 1 & 1 & 5
\end{array}
$$

61 Uncle Bungle Moves to Addition

(a)	(b)	(c)	(d)	(e)
	6	3	2	3
	9	6	0	6
2	3	2	5	6

Consider (e). If one digit was too large and the other too small we should have $4 + 5 = 9$, or $2 + 7 = 9$. But the result of adding cannot be greater than 7. $\therefore$ it must be $2 + 5 = 7$ (and note that there is not one to carry).

Consider (d). The 0 must become 1, and the 2 must also go up, making $3 + 1 = 4$ (again note that there is not one to carry).

Consider (c). This can only be $4 + 7 = 11$ (and note that there is one to carry).

Consider (b). $6 + 9 + 1 = 16$. This must be made smaller: $5 + 8 + 1 = 14$. And the 2 at the beginning of the last line becomes 1.

Complete solution

	5	4	3	2
	8	7	1	5
1	4	1	4	7

62 A Cross Number ★★

Consider 3 Across and 1 Down. 3 Across cannot be more than 99, ∴ 1 Down cannot be more than 198. If 3 Across started with 90 or less, 1 Down would start with 180 or less, and it would not be possible for the first digit of 3 Across and the second digit of 1 Down to be the same. If 3 Across is 95, 1 Down would be 190. But there are no 0's, ∴ 3 Across is 96 or more.

1 Across is a square of an odd number, and since it starts with 1, it must be the square of 11 or 13. If 11, then the first digit of 2 Down would be 2, and the second digit 6 or more – but this is not possible (see 2 Down), ∴ 1 Across is the square of 13 (169) and 2 Down can only be 678.

∴ since 3 Across is 97, 1 Down is 194.

∴ 4 Across is 484.

Complete solution

¹ 1	² 6	9
³ 9	7	▨
⁴ 4	8	4

63 Addition ★★

Letters for Digits, Two Numbers

(a)	(b)	(c)	(d)	(e)	(f)	(g)	(h)	(i)
	Y	A	B	A	E	W	T	P
	Y	A	W	H	P	T	T	H

| J | P | K | P | J | E | Y | A | H |

The first figure in the answer must be 1. ∴ J = 1.

Consider (i). P + H = H. ∴ P = 0. ∴ since the first two figures of the answer are 10, Y = 5.

Consider (g). Y = 5, and since P = 0 there cannot be anything to carry on to the next line (E + 0 = E). ∴ W and T are both less than 5, ∴ in (h) T + T is less than 10. ∴ W + T = 5. Neither of them can be 1, for J = 1; ∴ one of them is 2 and the other 3 (but we cannot yet say which is which).

Consider (c). We know that there is nothing to carry, and that A is not 1, 2, or 3, ∴ A = 4.
∴ from (h) T = 2, ∴ W = 3.
From (e) H = 7, and there is one to carry. ∴ in (d) B must be 6. ∴ there is one to carry on to (c), ∴ K = 9. ∴ by elimination, E = 8.

Complete solution

```
   5 4 6 4 8 3 2 0
   5 4 3 7 0 2 2 7
 ──────────────────
 1 0 9 0 1 8 5 4 7
```

64 Division ★★

Some Missing Figures

```
                    – 7 –        (a)
          – – )– – – – 1         (b)
            – – 4               (c)
           ───────
            – – –              (d)
             – –               (e)
           ───────
              – –              (f)
              – –              (g)
           ───────
```

(e) is the divisor times 7, and when subtracted from – – – it leaves only one figure. ∴ (e) must be at least 91.

The divisor cannot be as much as 15, for $7 \times 15 = 105$. And since (f) and (g) end in 1 (last figure of (b)), ∴ divisor is odd. ∴ it must be 13 (not 11 for 11×9 is only 99 and there are three figures in (c)).

∴ (c) must be $13 \times 8 \ (= 104)$.

And since (f) and (g) end in 1, they must be 91.

Add up from the bottom and we get:

Complete solution

```
              8 7 7
      1 3 )1 1 4 0 1
          1 0 4
         ───────
            1 0 0
              9 1
           ───────
                9 1
                9 1
           ───────
```

65 Right or Wrong? ★★

(i) *Let us first assume that all statements are true.*

From B's statement, B was second or third.

From E's statement, A was higher than B; and from A's statement C was higher than A.

∴ the first three must be C, A, B in that order.

From C's statement, D was higher than E.

∴ the order is:

1 C
2 A
3 B
4 D
5 E

(ii) *Assume now that all statements are false.*

From D's statement, D was first, second or third, but from C's statement, E was higher than D, ∴ D was second or third, and E was first or second.

From B's statement, B was first, fourth or fifth; but, from E's statement, B was not fifth; and, from A's statement, A was not fifth, ∴ B was not fourth. ∴ B was first.

∴ E was second, and D was third. And from A's statement, A was fourth and C was fifth.

Complete solution

(i) 1 Charlie
    2 Alf
    3 Bert
    4 Duggie
    5 Ernie

(ii) 1 Bert
    2 Ernie
    3 Duggie
    4 Alf
    5 Charlie

66 Football

Four Teams, Old Method

Consider C. They lost one, and since only 1 goal was scored against them, the score in this match was 0–1. They only played two, ∴ the score in their other match was 3–0.

   Consider B. After drawing two matches they must have as many goals for as against, ∴ they cannot have played a third match, for this would have made their goals for more or less than the goals scored against them.

∴ B only played two (and drew both); ∴ B did not play C.

∴ C's two matches were against A and D.

And B's two matches were against A and D.

A only played two, ∴ A did not play D.

   The score in C's two matches was 3–0 and 0–1, but D only had 2 goals against them. ∴ C v. D was 0–1; and C v. A was 3–0.

D's other match against B was drawn. ∴ the score was 2–2.

∴ B v. A was 3–3.

Complete solution

   A v. B   3–3
   A v. C   0–3
   B v. D   2–2
   C v. D   0–1

67 Cricket ★★

Three Teams

A gets 12 points from two matches. They must either get 6 points from each match (wins on first innings), or they must win one (10 points) and get 2 points from the other for a drawn match.

Suppose that they get 6 points from each match. Then C gets 2 points from the match with A, ∴ C gets 8 points from the match with B. But there is no way of getting 8 points from a match. ∴ our assumption is wrong, and A's 12 points must be 10 for a win and 2 for a draw.

Suppose that A v. B was a win (10 points), and A v. C 2 points. Then C gets 6 points from the match against A, and must therefore get 4 points from the match against B, so that B gets 4 points too (a tie on first innings). ∴ B gets only 4 points – but we know that B got 6 points.
∴ our assumption is wrong, ∴ A v. C was a win.
∴ A got 2 points against B, ∴ B got 6 points against A, and no points against C, ∴ C won against B.

Complete solution

   A v. B   B won on first innings
   A v. C   A won
   B v. C   C won

68 Letters for Digits ★★

A Multiplication

$$\begin{array}{cccc}
(a) & (b) & (c) & (d) \\
W & V & G & E \\
 & & & W \\
\hline
T & F & E & W
\end{array}$$

We know that W is odd. Suppose that W was 5; then since
the first digit of (a) is 5, and 5 × 5 = 25, ∴ there would be 5
digits in the answer, not 4. ∴ W is less than 5. It cannot be
1, for the answer would then be the same as the number to
be multiplied, ∴ W = 3.

And since the last figure of the answer is also W, E = 1,
and there is nothing to carry to (c). ∴ from (c), 3 times G
ends in 1, ∴ G = 7, and since 3 × 7 = 21, there is 2 to carry.

Since 3 × 3 = 9, T = 9, and 3 times V must be at least 2
less than 10. We know that there are no 0's. And V cannot
be 1, for E is 1. ∴ V = 2, and F = 8.

Complete solution

$$\begin{array}{cccc}
3 & 2 & 7 & 1 \\
 & & & 3 \\
\hline
9 & 8 & 1 & 3
\end{array}$$

69 A Cross Number ★★

5 Across is a perfect square, and from 4 Down and 2 Down both the digits are even. Two-figure perfect squares are 16, 25, 36, 49, 64 and 81. But the only one with both digits even is 64, ∴ 5 Across is 64.

4 Down is a multiple of 11, ∴ it must be 66. ∴ 3 Across is 468 and 2 Down is 984.

Sum of digits of 1 Across is 11, ∴ it is 119. And 1 Down is 141.

Complete solution

¹ 1	¹ 1	² 9
³ 4	⁴ 6	8
1	⁵ 6	4

70 Addition ★★

Letters for Digits, Three Numbers

	(a)	(b)	(c)	(d)	(e)	(f)
		Y	R	R	M	P
		Y	R	P	M	P
		Y	R	Y	M	P
	R	Y	M	A	B	P

Consider (*f*). P must be 0 or 5.

The most that can be carried when three digits are added together is 2 (9 + 9 + 9 = 27).

∴ R = 1 or 2.

∴ R + R + R cannot be more than 6. ∴ there is nothing to carry from (*c*) to (*b*). ∴ Y must be 5 and R = 1.

And since Y = 5, ∴ P = 0.

Consider (*d*). We know that R = 1, P = 0 and Y = 5.

∴ there is nothing to carry, ∴ M = 3.

∴ from (*e*) B = M + M + M = 9 (and there is nothing to carry to (*d*)).

∴ A = R + P + Y = 6.

Complete solution

```
  5 1 1 3 0
  5 1 0 3 0
  5 1 5 3 0
-----------
1 5 3 6 9 0
```

71 Uncle Bungle Passes through a Bad Patch ★ ★

$$
\begin{array}{r}
- 2 \quad (a) \\
5 - \overline{)5 - - -} \quad (b) \\
- - - \quad (c) \\
\hline
- - \quad (d) \\
- 9 \quad (e)
\end{array}
$$

If divisor is 5– then the second figure in (*a*) cannot be 2, for 2 times 5– comes to more than 100. If the second figure in (*a*) is 2, then the second figure in (*e*) cannot be 9. ∴ either 5 in divisor or 2 in (*a*) is wrong, and either 9 in (*e*) or 2 in (*a*) is wrong. But only one figure is wrong, so it must be 2 in (*a*). ∴ all the other figures are right, ∴ the divisor is 59, and the second figure in (*a*) should be 1.

Since 59 × 8 is only 472, (*c*) must be 59 × 9, i.e. 531.

Add up from the bottom and we have:

Complete solution

```
        9 1
  5 9 ) 5 3 6 9
        5 3 1
        ─────
          5 9
          5 9
```

72 Multiply by 5 ★★★

(*a*)	(*b*)	(*c*)	(*d*)	(*e*)	(*f*)	(*g*)
X	Q	R	X	F	X	A
						5

| A | M | Q | K | D | F | Q |

If X were 2, there would be another figure in the answer (5 × 2 = 10). ∴ X = 1.

When a number is multiplied by 5 the result ends in 0 or in 5. ∴ in (*g*) Q is 0 or 5.

Suppose Q = 0. Then, in (*b*), Q is 0, ∴ there can be nothing to carry to (*a*), ∴ A would be 5 (for X = 1). But if, in (*g*), A is 5, then Q would also be 5.

∴ our assumption is wrong, and Q = 5, not 0.

Consider (*a*). $5 \times 1 = 5$, and 2 is carried from (*b*). ∴ A = 7. ∴ the last two digits in the | answer are 85 (17×5), and F = 8. ∴ in (*e*) $5 \times 8 = 40$, and since there is nothing to carry D = 0. Since there is 4 to carry to (*d*) K = 9 (5 + 4), and there is nothing to carry to (*c*). ∴ in (*c*) R must be odd (5 times an even number ends in 0). But the only odd number left is 3. ∴ R = 3. And M = 6 (5 + 1).

Complete solution

```
 1 5 3 1 8 1 7
             5
 ─────────────
 7 6 5 9 0 8 5
```

73 Uncle Bungle gets 'One in Three' Wrong ★ ★ ★

```
            7 -      (a)
    - 5 )─ ─ ─        (b)
          ─ ─        (c)
          ───
          ─ ─ ─      (d)
          ─ ─ 8      (e)
          ─────
```

Look first for figure that is wrong. If divisor were 15 (and it cannot be less) then (*c*) would be $15 \times 7 = 105$. But this is not possible for (*c*) has two figures.
∴ either the 5 or the 7 is wrong.

If divisor ends in 5, then (*e*) cannot end in 8. ∴ either the 5 or the 8 is wrong.

But we know that only one figure is wrong, ∴ it must be the 5 in divisor. And 7 and 8 are correct.

(c) is the divisor times 7. ∴ the divisor is 14 or less (14 × 7 = 98). But if (c) were 98 or 91 (13 × 7), there would not be a first figure for (d).

And if divisor were 11, then since 11 × 9 = 99, there would not be three figures in (d).

∴ divisor is 12, (c) is 84, and (d) and (e) are 108 (12 × 9).

Add up from the bottom and we get:

Complete solution

```
        7 9
  1 2 ) 9 4 8
        8 4
      ───────
      1 0 8
      1 0 8
      ───────
```

★ ★ ★

74 A Cross Number

The second digit of 5 Across is even, ∴ the third digit of 3 Down is even.

∴ all digits of 3 Down are even ('each digit is 2 greater than one before').

∴ last digit of 3 Down must be 6 or 8 (not 4 for 3 Down would then be 024). But it cannot be 6, for the last digit of 1 Across would then be 2, but no perfect square ends in 2.

∴ 3 Down is 468 and 5 Across is 38.

The first digit of 4 Across must be 6. ∴ 1 Down ('A perfect square') is either 16 or 36. Suppose it is 36: then 1 Across must be 324 (18 squared). And 2 Down would be 2–3. But the sum of the digits of 2 Down is 16, and this is not possible (the second digit would have to be 11).

∴ 1 Down must be 16 (not 36).

And 1 Across (a perfect square) is 1–4, ∴ 144.
∴ 2 Down is 493.

Complete solution

1	2	3
1	4	4
4		
6	9	6
/////	5	
/////	3	8

75 Addition ★★★

Letters for Digits, Two Numbers

	(a)	(b)	(c)	(d)	(e)
	X	J	D	F	C
	C	D	F	C	C
	J	J	J	Y	J

From (e) J is even (C + C). ∴ in (a) X = C − 1, and there
must be 1 to carry from the second line down. In (b) (J + D)
cannot equal (10 + J), ∴ there is 1 to carry from (c), and D
= 9. J cannot be 2, for in (a) C would then be 1 and X would
be 0. But it does not make sense to have 0 in (a).

If J were 8, then (b) would be 8 + 9 + 1 (carried) = 18.
And F in (c) would have to be either 8 or 9. But D = 9, and
we are assuming that J is 8. ∴ J cannot be 8.

Suppose J = 6. Then we have:

201

$$2\ 6\ 9\ 7\ 3$$
$$3\ 9\ 7\ 3\ 3$$
$$\overline{6\ 6\ 6\ -\ 6}$$

And (d) would end in 0, and there would be 1 to carry. But there cannot be 1 to carry ($9 + 7 = 16$).

∴ our assumption is wrong. ∴ J must be 4.

∴ C = 2, X = 1, F = 5 and Y = 7.

Complete solution

$$1\ 4\ 9\ 5\ 2$$
$$2\ 9\ 5\ 2\ 2$$
$$\overline{4\ 4\ 4\ 7\ 4}$$

76 Bert was not First ★★★

Since C was as many places below F as B was above A, and the difference between C and F was more than 1,

∴ F and B cannot be fifth or sixth; and C and A cannot be first or second.

We also know that B was not first, F was not fourth and neither A nor C was sixth.

∴ the possibilities are:

1			D	E	F
2	B		D	E	F
3	A	B	C	D	E	F
4	A	B	C	D	E
5	A		C	D	E
6			D	E

We also know that the number of D's place was half the number of E's.

∴ D was first, second or third, and E was second, fourth or sixth.

∴ D was not sixth, ∴ E was sixth, ∴ D was third.

∴ F was first (no one else can be). ∴ B was second (no one else can be).

And since F is as many places above C as B is above A, ∴ C must be fourth and A must be fifth.

Complete solution

1 Fred
2 Bert
3 Duggie
4 Charlie
5 Alf
6 Ernie

77 Football ★★★

Five Teams, Old Method

Since the total of goals for must be the same as the total of goals against, ∴ B scored no goals. C played two and lost one, and had 7 goals for and 4 against. ∴ C must have won their other game.

Neither A, D nor E drew any, ∴ no match was drawn. And since B cannot have won any (they scored no goals), ∴ B played only one match and the score was 0–5. Neither A nor D scored as many as 5 goals, and though E scored 5 they could not all have been against B for they won 2 matches. ∴ B's match was against C and the score was 0–5.

C only played two, ∴ C lost their other match 2–4. ∴ C's other match was against E (the only other team that scored as many as 4 goals).

∴ C v. E was 2–4. And we have:

	A	B	C	D	E
A					
B			0-5		
C		5-0			2-4
D					
E			4-2		

D won one match and their goals were 2–2, ∴ they must have lost one (we know that they cannot have played more than two).

∴ D played A and E, and since E had 5 goals for and 3 against, this leaves 1–0 for E's other match or matches. But since there were no draws, E can only have played one other match.

∴ E v. D was 1–0, D v. A was 2–1, and E did not play A.

Complete solution

 A v. D 1–2
 B v. C 0–5
 C v. E 2–4
 D v. E 0–1

78 Division ★★★

Letters for Digits

```
        k n m d     (a)                    - - - -
  h e ) e n d j n   (b)            - - ) - - - - -
      c g           (c)                    - -
      ___                                  ___
      k d           (d)                    - -
      d k           (e)                    - -
      ___                                  ___
        p j         (f)                    - -
        g m         (g)                    - -
        ___                                ___
          m n       (h)                    - -
          m h       (i)                    - -
          ___                              ___
            h       (j)                      -
            ___                              ___
```

(The reader is advised to draw a figure, like the one on the
right above, where the digits can be inserted as they are
found.)

(*c*), (*e*), (*g*) and (*i*) are the divisor multiplied by four
different figures none of which is 1. If the divisor started
with 2, one of these multiples would be at least 100. ∴
divisor must start with 1, ∴ h = 1. ∴ from (*h*), (*i*) and
(*j*) n = 2. (*e*) is 1– multiplied by 2 (the second figure of (*a*)),
∴ d = 3 (it cannot be 2), ∴ in (*d*) k = 4. From (*d*), (*e*) and
(*f*) p = 9, ∴ in (*g*) g = 8. (*e*), 34, is the divisor multiplied by
2, ∴ e = 7, ∴ in (*c*) c = 6. The only figures left are 0 and 5.
From (*h*) and (*i*) m = 5, ∴ j = 0.

Complete solution

```
              4 2 5 3
    1 7 ) 7 2 3 0 2
          6 8
          ———
          4 3
          3 4
          ———
            9 0
            8 5
            ———
              5 2
              5 1
              ———
                1
```

79 Cricket

Four Teams

A must have 20 points from two wins, and 5 points for a tie (there is no other possibility). But B cannot have tied any (only 2 points); and C cannot have tied any (if C had got 5 points for a tie there is no way in which they could have got their other 3 points)

∴. A v. D was a tie and A must have won their other two matches against B and against C.

So we have:

	A	B	C	D
A	✕	10	10	5
B	0	✕		
C	0		✕	
D	5			✕

B cannot have lost their match against C, for C would then have got 10 points. But C only got 8. ∴ B got their 2 points from their match against C, and D beat B. C v. D was a win on the first innings for D (6 points for D and 2 for C).

Complete solution

    A v. B   A won
    A v. C   A won
    A v. D   tie
    B v. C   C won on first innings
    B v. D   D won
    C v. D   D won on first innings

Letters for Digits, Three Numbers

(a)	(b)	(c)	(d)	(e)	(f)	(g)
G	G	J	D	G	F	F
G	G	G	P	B	F	F
G	G	B	D	G	F	F
Z	N	Y	H	P	B	G

G must be 1, 2 or 3 (if it were 4 or more there would be another letter before Z in the answer).

If G = 3, then from (g) F would be 1, ∴ B would also be 3. ∴ G is not 3.

If G = 1, then F = 7 (7 + 7 + 7 = 21), and B in (f) would be 3 but Z = 3 (1 + 1 + 1) and B and Z cannot be the same. ∴ G is not 1 ∴ G = 2, and F = 4 (4 + 4 + 4 = 12), and from (f) B = 3. From (a) Z = 6, and from (b) N = 7 (there cannot be more than 1 to carry from (c)).

From (e) P = 2 + 3 + 2 + 1 (that has been carried) = 8. From (d) D + 8 + D = H, ∴ H = 0 or is even. But we know what 2, 4, 6 and 8 are, ∴ H = 0, ∴ D = 1 (and there is 1 to carry). The only digits left are 5 and 9. ∴ J = 9 and Y = 5.

Complete solution

```
2 2 9 1 2 4 4
2 2 2 8 3 4 4
2 2 3 1 2 4 4
─────────────
6 7 5 0 8 3 2
```

81 A Cross Number ★★★

4 Down (two figures) is the square root of 5 Across (three figures), ∴ 4 Down must be less than 32 ($32^2 = 1024$). But the first figure of 4 Down cannot be 1 or 3 (3 Across is even). ∴ 4 Down is 2–.

And the second figure of 4 Down must be the same when squared, ∴ it must be 1, 5 or 6. But not 1, for the second digit of 4 Down is greater than the first.
∴ 4 Down is 25 or 26, and 5 Across is 625 or 676.
But the second figure of 5 Across cannot be 2 (see 2 Down).
∴ 5 Across is 676 and 4 Down is 26. And 2 Down is 357.
∴ 1 Across is 13 (5 Across is $2 \times 2 \times 13 \times 13$).
And 1 Down is 186.

Complete solution

¹ 1	² 3	▨
³ 8	5	⁴ 2
⁵ 6	7	6

Four Teams, New Method

Four matches have been played (six minus the two that have not been played).

∴ 40 points were given for wins or draws.

∴ C must have 30, and must have won all their matches.

And A and B must have got 5 each, ∴ A v. B was a draw.

And D only played one match (against C).

So we have:

	A	B	C	D
A		dr.	l.	
B	dr.		l.	
C	w.	w.		w.
D			l.	

∴ D got 3 goals against C. ∴ the score was 3–4 (not more than 7 goals were scored in any match).

A got 5 points for a draw, ∴ scored 2 goals.

∴ A v. B was 1–1; and A v. C was 1–?.

B got 5 points for a draw, ∴ scored 3 goals. ∴ B v. C was 2–?. C scored 9 goals, four of them against D, and since they won all their matches, C v. A was 2–1; and C v. B was 3–2.

Complete solution

A v. B 1–1
A v. C 1–2
B v. C 2–3
C v. D 4–3

83 Our Factory – Logic and Charm ★ ★ ★

Read through (1), (2), (3) and (4) carefully and you will see that the information given about logic and charm is as follows:

Order	Logic					Charm				
1					C					A
2	B		A	C		D			C	A
3	B	D	E	A	C	D	B		C	A
4		D	E	A	C	D	B	E	C	A
5		D		A			B		C	

C is first in logic, and A is first in charm (no one else can be).
 Charm. E is fourth (the only possible place).
And since E is below B, B is third.
∴ C is fifth (no one else can be). ∴ D is second (the only place left).

211

Logic. If E were third, then B would be second, and D would be fourth or fifth. But B is only one place above D (see (1), and see order for charm).

∴ E must be fourth, B second and D third.

∴ A is fifth.

Complete solution

	Logic	Charm
1	Charlie	Alf
2	Bert	Duggie
3	Duggie	Bert
4	Ernie	Ernie
5	Alf	Charlie

84 Bungle Blunders ★★★

$$\begin{array}{r} 8 - \quad\ (a) \\ -2 \overline{)--6} \quad (b) \\ -5 \quad\ (c) \\ \hline --\quad\ (d) \\ --\quad\ (e) \end{array}$$

Look first for the figure that is wrong. The divisor and (c) cannot both be right, for no multiple of −2 can end in 5.

And if 8 is correct then (c) would be even.

∴ either 8 or 5 is wrong.

But only one figure is wrong; ∴ 5 is wrong, and the other three figures are correct.

∴ (c) is (−2 × 8), and this can only be 96.

And the divisor is 12.

(*d*) and (*e*) end in 6, and must therefore be either 96 or 36. But if (*d*) were 96, there would have to be an extra figure at the beginning of (*b*). ∴ (*d*) and (*e*) are 36.

Add up from the bottom and we get:

Complete solution

$$
\begin{array}{r}
8\ 3 \\
1\ 2\ \overline{)9\ 9\ 6} \\
9\ 6 \\
\hline
3\ 6 \\
3\ 6 \\
\hline
\end{array}
$$

85 Cricket ★★★

Five Teams

(i) No one can play more than four matches. Since B got 35 points they must have played four, won three (30 points) and tied one (5 points). B's tied match was not against E (only 2 points) and against A (6 points and they cannot be 5 + 1). We know that D (12 points) won one of their matches, ∴ they cannot have tied with B, for they would then have got at least 15 points. ∴ B's tied match was against C, and they won the other three.

(ii) D won one match. Not against B (who lost none); not against A (who only played two, losing one against B and scoring 6 points from the other); and not against C (who tied with B and got 6 points from the other match they played). ∴ D must have won against E.

(iii) A's second match was a win on the first innings, and C's second match was a win on the first innings. ∴ A did not play C.

(iv) E got 2 points; this can only have been in their match against A. ∴ A v. E was a win on the first innings for A. And since A only played two, A did not play D. And C's other match was a win on the first innings against D.

Complete solution
A v. B   B won
A v. E   A won on first innings
B v. C   tie
B v. D   B won
B v. E   B won
C v. D   C won on first innings
D v. E   D won

86 Addition   ★★★

Letters for Digits, Three Numbers

(a)	(b)	(c)	(d)	(e)	(f)	(g)	(h)
B	Y	T	Z	B	X	D	D
B	S	V	Z	D	B	D	D
B	B	S	Z	D	B	D	D
X	V	N	P	P	N	B	B

Since in (a) B + B + B is less than 10, ∴ B = 1, 2 or 3.

Suppose B was 1. Then from (h) D would have to be 7 (7 + 7 + 7 = 21), ∴ in (g) (7 + 7 + 7 + 2) would be 23. ∴ B is not 1.

Suppose B was 2. Then from (h) D would have to be 4 (4 + 4 + 4 = 12), ∴ in (g) (4 + 4 + 4 + 1) would be 13. ∴ B is not 2.

∴ B = 3, ∴ D = 1 and X = 9. And from (*f*) N = 5 (9 + 3 + 3 = 15, and there is one to carry).

From (*e*) P = 6 (3 + 1 + 1 + 1 = 6). From (*d*) Z + Z + Z = 6, ∴ Z = 2. From (*c*) T + V + S = 15 (not 5, for the only two digits left which are less than 5 are 0 and 4; and not 25, for the three largest digits left are 8, 7 and 4 which add up to 19). It is easy to see that T, V and S must be 0, 7 and 8, but we cannot yet say which is which.

∴ in (*b*) Y = 4, and since there is nothing to carry to (*a*), ∴ S = 0, V = 8 and T = 7.

Complete solution

```
3 4 7 2 3 9 1 1
3 0 8 2 1 3 1 1
3 3 0 2 1 3 1 1
───────────────
9 8 5 6 6 5 3 3
```

87 What Done It? ★ ★ ★

Call:

windscreen wiper	A
open left window	B
put on handbrake	C
pull the button that says 'Push Heater'	D
open right window	E
high-pitched scream	p
rumble	q
dull thud	r

Then we have:

B, C, E	→ p, q	(i)
A, C, D, E	→ q, r	(ii)
A, B, C, D	→ p, r	(iii)
A, B, C, E	→ p, q, r	(iv)

(Remember that if, for example, B → p then whenever p is on the right B must be on the left, and when p is *not* on the right B *cannot* be on the left.)

Let us look for where p is not.

In (ii) p is not on the right, ∴ p is not caused by A, C, D or E. ∴ p must be caused by B (and we check by seeing that B is on the left in (i), (iii) and (iv)).

In (iii) q is not on the right, ∴ q is not caused by A, B, C or D. ∴ q must be caused by E (and we check by seeing that E is on the left in (i), (ii) and (iv)).

From (iv) D cannot be the cause of p, q or r.

And in (i) r is not on the right, ∴ r is not caused by B, C or E.

∴ r must be caused by A (and we check by seeing that A is on the left in (ii), (iii) and (iv)).

Complete solution

The high-pitched scream is caused by opening the left window.

The rumble is caused by opening the right window.

The dull thud is caused by the windscreen wiper.

88 Uncle Bungle Multiplies ★★★

$$
\begin{array}{ccccc}
(a) & (b) & (c) & (d) & (e) \\
 & 1 & 6 & 6 & 3 \\
 & & & & 3 \\
\hline
2 & 1 & 3 & 7 & 9 \\
\hline
\end{array}
$$

The last figure in the answer can only be 8. To get 8 the first figure in (e) could be 4, and the second could be 2; or the first figure in (e) could be 2 and the second could be 4. But if the second figure in (e) were 2, then, since the first figure in (b) can only be 2, there would be only four figures, not five, in the answer. ∴ in (e), the second 3 must be 4, and the first must be 2.

If the first figure in (d) was 5, then the second would have to be 0; but it cannot be. ∴ the first figure in (d) is 7, and the second is 8. (Note that there is now 2 to carry.)

If the first figure in (c) was 7, then the second would have to be 8 + 2, but it is 2 or 4. But if the first figure in (c) was 5, then the second would be 0 + 2, which is all right.

The first figure in (b) must be 2; ∴ the first two figures of the answer must be 8 + 2 = 10.

Complete solution

$$
\begin{array}{r}
2\ 5\ 7\ 2 \\
4 \\
\hline
1\ 0\ 2\ 8\ 8 \\
\hline
\end{array}
$$

Four Teams, New Method

The points which A, B, C and D got might be divided as follows:

	Wins or draws	Goals
A	5	2
B	10	3
C	15	5
D	—	4

Each team played at least one game for they all got some points. If the wins and draws were as above, then three games were played ($5 + 10 + 15 = 30$). And there cannot be more. If only two games were played then no team could have played more than one, and C would have got at least 10 points for goals.

∴ three games were played, and the table above is correct.

We are told that at least 2 goals were scored by each side in a drawn match. ∴ B cannot have got their points from two draws (they would then have got at least 14 points).

∴ A v. C was a draw, and B and C both won one (three matches altogether). And with 4 goals and no points D must have been beaten by both B and C. ∴ A only played once (against C), and the score was 2–2.

C v. D was 3–?. And B v. D was 3–?. And since D lost both these matches and scored 4 goals, ∴ the score in each was 3–2.

Complete solution
A v. C   2–2
B v. D   3–2
C v. D   3–2

90 Addition

★ ★ ★

Letters for Digits, Three Numbers

	(a)	(b)	(c)	(d)	(e)
	L	P	B	R	R
	T	L	S	R	R
	S	B	R	R	R
	R	L	M	P	L

Consider (a). R must be at least 6 (1 + 2 + 3). But if R were 6, then in (e) L would be 8; but L in (a) cannot be 8. ∴ R is not 6.

If R were 9, then in (e) L would be 7; but L in (a) cannot be 7. ∴ R is not 9. ∴ R is 7 or 8.

Suppose R = 7. Then L in (e) would be 1 (3 × 7 = 21); and P in (d) would be 3 ((3 × 7) + 2 = 23). In (b) we would have: 3(P) + 1(L) + B + (0, 1 or 2 to carry) = 10 + 1(L), (so that there would be 1 to carry to (a); but not 2, for B would then have to be more than 10). ∴ T and S would be between them 2 and 3. But we are assuming that P = 3. ∴ our assumption is wrong. ∴ R must be 8. ∴ L = 4. ∴ P = 6. And, since L = 4 and there is one to carry to (a), T and S must be between them 1 and 2.

In (b), since 2 is T or S and 4 is L, B must be 3. And in (c), since M cannot be 4, M must be 5, and S = 2, T = 1.

Complete solution

```
  4 6 3 8 8
  1 4 2 8 8
  2 3 8 8 8
  ─────────
  8 4 5 6 4
```

CODES FOR KIDS

Burton Albert jnr.

A fascinating collection of codes and cyphers for children of 7 to 11. Confound your enemies! Confuse your friends!

MY SECRET FILE

John Astrop

A cross between a file, a diary and a suggestions book. Sample subjects include an IF page (if I could live anywhere, I'd live . . .) and a Christmas Presents page (got what? gave what?).

BET YOU CAN'T!

Vicki Cobb and Kathy Darling

Bet you can't resist trying out some of these tempting tricks on your family and friends. And you'll win the bet every time with such scientific impossibilities. For despite looking dead easy, the basic principles of gravity, mechanics, maths, perception, liquids and energy ensure that they cannot actually be performed!

THE CALENDAR QUIZ BOOK

Barbara Gilgallon/Sue Samuels

Rather lively and inventive quiz book which uses the months and special days of the year as a framework on which to hang a wide variety of questions – not just testing general knowledge but encouraging the reader to find things out for himself.

THE PUFFIN TRIVIA QUIZ GAME BOOK

Maureen and Alan Hiron and David Elias

A mind-boggling collection of Trivia questions plus games for the younger members of the family. Carefully chosen and selected by three experts in this field, these questions are bound to baffle adult players but provide true equality for kids!

UP WITH SKOOL!

A collection of children's own worst school jokes. Each section is introduced by a celebrity, including Sir Harry Secombe on Games, Roald Dahl on Punishment and Cyril Smith, MP, on the delights of school dinners.

Johnny Ball's THINK BOX and
PLAYS FOR LAUGHS

Johnny Ball, whose TV shows have made maths a popular
subject with millions of children, shares his enthusiasm for
numbers in these fascinating books of puzzles, tricks and
brain teasers.

JOKE BOX

Gyles Brandreth

A serious but at the same time hilarious guide to being
funny. Full of examples which cannot fail to entertain.

THE PUFFIN BOOK OF CAR GAMES

Douglas P. St Barnard

A bumper collection of over 100 games to play and things to
do while you are travelling.